Forsytes, Pendyces
and Others

THE WORKS OF
JOHN GALSWORTHY

NOVELS

THE GROVE EDITION
The Novels, Stories, and Studies of John Galsworthy in small volumes

Forsytes, Pendyces and Others

By
JOHN GALSWORTHY

With a Foreword
by
ADA GALSWORTHY

NEW YORK
CHARLES SCRIBNER'S SONS
1935

CONTENTS

v

Contents

FOREWORD

The material, varied and rather unusual, contained in this volume, has been selected with much care and more trepidation. It is presented with a certain confidence, nonetheless, in the belief that there will be found much of interest therein, though for very varying reasons.

None of it has hitherto been published (otherwise than serially) except the one short story: 'The Doldrums.' Of that, more anon.

Danaë, the first item, formed originally the beginning of the novel that we now know as 'The Country House.' In it we meet many who, later on, become our intimate acquaintances: Here are Forsytes, old Jolyon, young Jolyon, James, and George; here are Mr. Horace Pendyce and Gregory Vigil from 'The Country House'; Danaë (later Helen) Bellew, who, we realise, has even more affinity with Rosamund Larne of 'The Stoic' and 'Old English'; Jaspar Bellew, a slight sketch but remarkably vivid; their two children; Anthony Thornworthy (Danaë's father), a blend of Anthony in 'Strife' and of Sylvanus Heythorp in 'The Stoic' and 'Old English'; Hemmings, Secretary of Companies; a faint foreshadowing of Mrs. Megan in 'The Pigeon' and even of that other, more lovable, Megan in 'The Apple Tree.' Their literary foundations are well and truly laid, fit for future building on.

Following this early sidelight on our author's work come six short stories, all of post-war date, and mature in style. Then, one very short nightmare, and three idyllic moments, re-creations of child-life and of country-life.

'The Doldrums' taken out of 'From the Four Winds' (a volume no longer accessible to the general reader) has a special interest, it is felt, not from its value as a piece of writing—the date, 1896, may perhaps disarm criticism on that score—as from the fact that it gives us true and striking portraits of Conrad, at that time first mate of a sailing ship of the English Merchant Service, and of the narrator, Galsworthy, a young barrister studying Navigation with a view to its application to intricate cases at the Admiralty Bar, a branch of the legal profession towards which he was so ingenuously headed. Neither of the two men at that time had any intention of taking Literature as a profession (though Conrad had a rough and unrevised MS. with him, which in due course took shape as 'Allmeyer's Folly'). The subject of 'The Doldrums' was enacted under their eyes, the opium-ridden doctor dying on that voyage and being buried at sea.

Part II has been carefully chosen for its personal appeal; its notes and appreciations range from one on a very gifted young actress who died at the age of 24 to one on Mr. W. Shakespeare.

Part III speaks for itself; attention need only be drawn to its dates. The young light-hearted squib called: 'The Winter Garden' was, so far as memory serves, written in 1908. The unacted scene of 'Escape' was written in 1926; 'The Golden Eggs' (a fragment) was written either in Arizona in 1925 or in South Africa in 1926; and 'Similes,' written in the autumn of 1932—the author's last work.

Now but one word more—and that word Caveat! May it be recalled to mind and applied in all seriousness when reading the orthodox and unorthodox views held by characters in fiction! An imaginative writer should be forgiven if, now and then, his characters ride off on their own half-tamed steeds; nor is their author primarily a theologian, philosopher, or politician; he is but—an imaginative writer!

ADA GALSWORTHY.

February 5, 1935

CAVEAT

It has become the fashion for authors to preface their books with the words: 'None of the characters in the novel are drawn from life.' They might with advantage enter a more important caveat: 'The Author should not be identified with the views expressed by any of his characters.'

CHAPTER I

AN INTRODUCTORY AFTERNOON

IN the Board-room of the Bhang and Sciatic, on the second floor of a mansion in Cannon Street, one afternoon of November, 1890, an odour of turbot, sauce mousseline, of apple tart, and Camembert cheese pervaded an atmosphere already tempered by a hot fire, some fine samples of the Company's india-rubber in its more primitive conditions, and the prolonged presence of a Chairman, Secretary, and five Directors.

The Meeting was over, but old Anthony Thornworthy, solitary in his Chairman's seat, stayed with closed eyes, as if recovering the power of thought. His large, bald, and perfectly round head shone under the electric light; the finger and thumb of the hand on the table still held a pen. Between the silver-white of his high, unwrinkled forehead and the silver-white of a round beard that concealed all vestige of neck, were cheeks the colour of apples. He breathed without noise; no movement stirred his bulky form. So some old Roman might have sat, renewing his power after a contest with the new School of thought.

For two hours had Anthony made front against his five colleagues, and by virtue of the strange power that lies in a fixed principle, the prestige of his long career, the glamour attaching to the advocacy of the bolder course, he had remained master of the field.

On the agenda, the issue was thus stated——a decision had

unfortunately no longer been postponable in accordance
with the safe traditions of the Board:

"Consider application of the workmen for higher wages.
Read correspondence with the Works officials in connection
therewith. Read letter from the Proofer's Union.

"Report the visit to the Works of Mr. Simon Harnutt,
of the Central Committee of Trades Unions."

Anthony's dictum at the commencement of the debate:
"The more you give them the more they will want. No
concessions," had pleased everyone. It was obvious that
the men's demands were unreasonable. It was known what
men were like. They were never satisfied. They were only
asking because the Bhang and Sciatic had, since its reconstruction two years back, paid large dividends. Trust men
for watching the price of rubber, and finding out the profit
made; trust men for wanting a bit themselves. There
was something both underhand and grasping about men's
conduct in thus taking advantage of the Company's pros-
perity. Thomas Brandwhite, Director of the firm of
Brandwhite and Brown, the leading rubber men, spoke
thus: "Ready enough to ask for a rise when times are good,
but as for a reduction in bad times—you may whistle for
that. I know them, they're all alike."

No words could more admirably have summed up the
cynicism of men's attitude; their unswerving attempts to
benefit themselves at the expense of shareholders, indirectly
at the expense of Directors whose prestige and, incidentally,
whose fees they endangered by such sinister demands.

A hum of approval went round the table, as every Director's private thought arose with whirring wings.

Then spoke the youngest Director, the Chairman's son
Solomon; his were the first words that disturbed the general harmony: "Why shouldn't the poor devils want to

benefit? I should, myself!" His tall stout form was thrown back in his chair, his chest was expanded, his thumbs buried in the upper pockets of his waistcoat; his large, round, clean-shaven face resembled a moon, and his fine eyes beamed good-naturedly from behind gold spectacles. He wore in his tie a diamond pin, on the little finger of his left hand a large gold seal ring.

Anthony Thornworthy looked fixedly at his son; and no one answered. It was only young Thornworthy, to whom indeed, though he sat now on three Directorates (of which one was a brewery) no one paid a great deal of attention in matters of business. Some called him a 'doctrinaire,' others a Radical; all agreed that he was amiable and harmless. He had passed through Harrow and Oxford without notoriety, and had eaten dinners at the Inner Temple. The habits of his mind and body had acquired him friends who had pushed him, characteristically unable to push himself, into one or two 'soft things.' He was still unmarried, and lived in rooms adjoining a famous Liberal Club, at whose open windows he could be seen seated, in the season, under a white top hat.

He beamed back at his father's eyes, thus fixed on him, and there was silence; for though no one attached importance to Solomon, his remark had brought nearer to each Director the inherent discomfort of men's demands.

Then Thomas Brandwhite said: "If they go out—a pretty mess we shall be in, with all those stocks half calledup, and rubber on the drop."

At these words James Forsyte raised his long visage framed in white Dundreary whiskers, and taking a shifting, anxious survey of surrounding facts, said: "Go out? Who says they're going out? Surely they won't go out! What do you say, Hemmings? You ought to know," thus hoping, in accordance with his guiding principle, to throw the burden of a decision upon the shoulders of the Secretary.

could write his name for a hundred thousand pounds.

And at this strong Board the Chairman looked, with small deep-set eyes niched in between his overhanging brows and his plum-apple coloured cheeks; what were they afraid of—not a backbone amongst the lot!

At the age of seventy-five, labouring under an accumulation of physical ailments, harassed by want of money, suspended indeed over the abyss of bankruptcy by the single rope of this very Bhang and Sciatic, old Thornworthy was conscious of more fight in his little finger than in all their bodies put together. This reflection gave him pleasure, and he looked at his son mockingly. It was difficult to believe that he was responsible for the entrance into the world of that big, soft, mooney, generalising chap! He had never had reason to suspect the virtue of his wife, a Welsh lady of the name of Meryon, who had given him, in Solomon and Danaë, two pledges of an extremely moderate affection. And so he looked steadily at his son. He had never known the fellow stand up for himself; he was always talking of 'the other side.' He had never known him hit out, he had never known him out of temper. He had never known him condemn anybody or anything, or come to any point whatever. Certainly he had never seen him show the white feather, or known him do a mean thing; but there was no 'go,' no push, no enterprise about him anywhere. He was a sort of professed heathen, too; for, though Anthony himself had not been to church since his wife's death, and had a contempt for parsons (whom he described as 'old women'), yet he was a strictly orthodox Christian, and regarded his son's opinions, if anything so soft could be described as opinions, as un-English. Those opinions did not, indeed, disturb him, for he was a philosopher; they merely excited his contempt, as a sign of a negative, self-sacrificing turn of mind. For himself he had but the one motto: 'Fight it out!' To this he had tuned his harp all his life long, necessarily when he was young, more necessarily now that he was old and had nothing left to live for but the comfort of never giving in.

And Anthony looked at his son. The Bhang and Sciatic paid good fees, or he would never have put Solomon on the Board; for with his mooney good-nature he was worse than useless. But Anthony had inherited the instincts of a father. His own father, Squire Baldwin Thornworthy of Bovey Tracey, in addition to Anthony and other offspring of wedlock, had had more children than any man in Devonshire. Hardly a parish in the county but had been enriched by the strain of Thornworthy, in those fine old days which were passed in an Omar-like worship of horses and women—books, the third article of that creed, having been exchanged for a more English article.

For all his contempt, Anthony was fond of his son, and found it not only convenient but necessary that that son should have an independent income. For many years his own position had been that of a tight-rope walker balancing before the public eye upon the narrow wire of Director's fees, holding his creditors at bay by the fear that should they, by their interference, cause him to fall from his giddy perch into the abyss of bankruptcy, they would deprive themselves even of the interest on their money which old Anthony's fees still enabled him to pay them. It was a defence characteristic of a man who had all his life faced facts and stared them out of countenance; and thanks to this cool and cynical courage, once and once only during the twenty years of his financial insecurity had he visibly wobbled. This was in the spring of 1888, when the Bhang and Sciatic, after a long period of depression, had shown unmistakable signs of collapse. Following his habit of taking the bull by the horns Anthony, instead of retirement or liquidation, had carried through a reconstruction on lines which had placed the Company once more in funds. It had been a hard fight, and so far crowned with exemplary success. He had been fortunate enough at that juncture to secure the very man who, in the position of Secretary, was most likely to foster the confidence of shareholders. Joseph (better known in the City, from the peculiar dignity of his posture, as 'Down-by-the-starn' Hemmings) had been compelled just then, by the obviously impending decline of the New Colliery Co. Ltd. to look about him. The promise of a salary of fifteen hundred a year had decided him to the wiser course of abandoning his ship before it abandoned him. As he said to his wife, with his coat-tails parted before the fire, in the drawing-room at Streatham: "I made the concern; it wouldn't become a man in my position to be obliged to go begging round the City for a post. I have to think of myself. I have to think of what's due to me; I know what I am. It's not right that a man in a thousand should be chucked out of his job for no fault of his. I know what I am." And Mrs. Hemmings, on the yellow tapestry sofa, drawn up at an elegant angle on the carpet covered with pink cabbages, had repeated: "Yes, Jos; yes, Jos."

On another evening he had not expressed himself so mildly. It was after the interview with his then Chairman, old Jolyon Forsyte, at which he had tendered his resignation. Striding about the Streatham drawing-room and kicking the legs of the furniture, his fine eyes alight with anger, he had blasphemed freely: "The old fool—he called me a sneak; the old ——! He talked about rats. If he'd been younger I'd have knocked that white head of his against the walls. I'd have given him 'rats'!" And Mrs. Hemmings, cowering on the sofa, had answered: "Yes, Jos; yes, Jos!" It was seldom that Streatham was called upon to pass through so psychological a moment.

To Anthony, his great ability and thorough mastery of accounts had proved of the utmost service. A chance meeting with his old friend Jolyon Forsyte at the Disunion Club might indeed have produced unpleasantness. For old Jolyon, very upright, and looking better than ever at eighty-three, with his great white drooping moustache, and his direct deep-grey eyes, had opened fire thus: "So you've got that precious sneak, Hemmings!" Anthony nodded, and through his little blue eyes there shone so shrewd and cynically humorous a gleam, that old Jolyon's eyes reflected it in a sudden twinkle. "Wish you joy of him!" he said. "After all, I don't know why the beggar shouldn't do the best he can for himself!" And again Anthony nodded. . . .

The dividend in March 1889 had been one of three shillings per share, or at the rate of fiteen per cent; in the following September the Board had declared an interim of a shilling. The year 1890 had seen the position still further strengthened, and it was upon an almost blue horizon that the cloud of these Labour troubles had gathered. In his precarious pecuniary position a strike in the Bhang and Sciatic factories might have very serious consequences for Anthony; a blow to his prestige in any direction might well bring the whole card-house down about his ears. His reason told him this (for he was a man of wide and even subtle reasoning powers), but there was in his soul something deeper and more powerful than reason—the instinct of battle, and autocracy, as high and stiff-necked as Haman; and, skirmish around as his reason might, bedded in the silent recesses of a soul firm as his native Dartmoor rocks, that instinct dwelt immovable.

He sat with eyes closed, utterly motionless, and at the green baize door the Secretary, a fine figure, bearded in iron-grey, stood watching him, an expression of half-contemptuous malevolence clouding his handsome eyes. Himself a masterful man, 'Down-by-the-starn' Hemmings had experienced the misfortune of falling out of the frying-pan into the fire. Old Jolyon Forsyte had been bad enough, Anthony Thornworthy was worse. Thus, he suffered continually the mortification of not, as he would have said it: "bossing the show." It was as though an absurd Fate, ignorant of the fitness of things, perhaps a little jealous, were for ever planting itself in the path of his deserts. In small, everyday matters he had his way of course, and the rest of the Board he held in the hollow of his hand; but, and herein lay the sting, in questions of large policy (of which he was so peculiarly fitted to judge) his Chairman sat there like the Czar of all the Russias, obstinate as an old pig, to knock up against whom was like knocking your head against a wall. With his superior commercial instinct 'Down-by-the-starn' knew well enough when he was on the losing side; knew well enough that in this dispute his Chairman had taken the wrong line, was courting disaster. He had not watched the rising strength of Labour and Unions for nothing. Hating 'men' with a hatred only felt by members of the clerk and shopkeeper class—a hatred that had its roots in the consciousness of too thin a barrier between himself and his 'inferiors,' he was all the more alive to the necessity of not opposing them except with victory in his trousers pockets. No more whole-hearted supporter of Capital was perhaps at that time alive than 'Down-by-the-starn' Hemmings, who had investments of his own in the Bhang and Sciatic, and in other enterprises where the success of Capital over Labour was vital. A member of the Church of England too—and churchwarden, he knew that the greatest danger to that edifice of which he was a pillar—to that body which guaranteed him his social position —lay in those irresponsible masses who had nothing to lose and everything to gain by nonconformity and by rebellion. As he would express himself among intimates at Streatham: "I'm a good Christian; it's my duty to extend peace and goodwill to all men; but as to these Socialists and Labour fellows—a set of ruffians—nonconformists to a man—I draw the line at them, that's flat; and what's more, I believe our Saviour would have, too." Nor could many be found in

Streatham to disagree with this sturdy British view of Christianity.

Among the factory hands no one could have been more unpopular; as he passed along the grimy sheds low-muttered wishes that his soul might repose in hell testified to a still stronger Christian spirit amongst his adversaries.

But at this moment he felt that no good purpose could be served by withstanding their demands, and it was with an irritation the deeper that it was grounded in fear, that he bore towards his Chairman the draft letter to the Manager of the Company's Works:

"DEAR SIR" (it ran),

"The Directors met to-day, and had under discussion the men's demands. While viewing the situation with considerable disquietude, they considered it inadvisable at the present moment to make the concessions asked for. You are instructed therefore to tell the men that the Directors regret that at the present time they cannot see their way to advancing the existing rates of wages.

I am, dear Sir,
Yours faithfully
JOS. HEMMINGS. (Sec.)"

And over the motionless Anthony he stood still. In those old days, before Commerce had civilised the world, when men by swift strokes attained their ends, Hemmings with one blow of his strong fist on the bald head beneath, would have sent to the Shades the soul of his Chairman. Now, with a touch on his shoulder and a deprecating smile, he did but place the document under his nose.

Anthony stirred; he made a sound in his depths—a sighing sound like the groan of an old tree. One eye unclosed, his hand moved the pen as though asking for it to be given drink; and, taking it from him, Hemmings dipped it in the pot. Slowly Anthony read the letter. With a scratch he drew his pen through it, then, in his slow large hand, wrote:

"At the Board Meeting to-day it was decided to reject the men's demands,"

and held it out to his Secretary without a word. Then, by the edge of the table pulling himself to his feet, he walked slowly towards the sideboard. There, with tumbler held out in his broad hand, mottled strangely with white patches as though half-dead, he invited the Secretary to give him the draught of brandy and soda which closed the labours of the day. And presently, with infinite slowness and care, he descended to the street.

The Secretary followed; it was a custom he never neglected. The old man was very feeble; he might topple over any day! And it was with a strange pleasure, as though venting a store of secret spite, that he made his wonted remark: "You'd better let me call you a four-wheeler, Sir!"

Anthony shook his head and with infinite slowness made his way out into the traffic, towards the Underground. He was a well-known figure on that platform; the porters nudged each other, and, as the train came in, one of them moved up close behind him. Anthony waved him aside. It was as good as a play to see the old fellow try to get into the train by himself! So—the porters to each other; but down in their hearts was a deep, unvoiced admiration for that vain, heroic effort renewed each day. And it was the most gentle, the most delicate of pushes that heaved the feeble, bulky form into its place.

CHAPTER II

LEANING back, motionless against the padded cushions of the railway carriage, Anthony mused. He was not a man who helped trouble to come by going to meet it; and he had lived too long on the brink of a financial volcano to suffer apprehension; moreover, in the last resort, he could always await death at Coombe Honey. For Anthony, in the days when his wife was alive, before his monetary troubles began, had, with his habitual astuteness, settled a farm which he had inherited from his father, upon his wife for life, with remainder to whomsoever she should appoint. In view of Anthony's monetary embarrassments she had, at his suggestion, appointed in favour of the Trustees of the settlement, Gregory Vigil, a man of unquestioned probity, who now held the property for the benefit of Anthony. And sometimes he would go down and stay there for the good of his health—on the borders of Dartmoor, under the shelter of that queer rock—Solomon's Chin; there was no better air in England.

But it was not of Coombe Honey, nor of the Bhang and Sciatic that Anthony was thinking. He thought of his daughter. Her position caused him at times considerable anxiety. The shrewd and daring cast of a mind which had never hesitated to face facts enabled him to know her perhaps better than anyone; and he did not exaggerate a situation which in women of less vitality than Danaë, would have been intolerable. He did full justice to her buoyancy, to her quality of getting a positive enjoyment out of the ups and downs of Fate, and making a positive luxury of her own misfortunes. But she had recently spoken of going on the stage, and this did not accord with Anthony's ideas of the dignity of a Thornworthy.

Married at an early age to Jaspar Bellew, their marital relations were now of a most anomalous order. They were not divorced, nor separated, but they did not live together. The children, Meryon and Thyme, belonged neither to one nor to the other. The boy Meryon was at school; and each, swooping down on him as the spirit moved them, would carry him off for the holidays. Bellew paid for the schooling, no doubt. Thyme lived with her mother, but there was no settled arrangement; Bellew made his wife no definite allowance, and for the last three years she had lived with her father. The situation taxed Anthony's cynical philosophy. It was not his business to dictate how they should live, but their relations were neither fish, flesh, fowl, nor good red herring. They would meet and be good enough friends; he would give Danaë money and presents; then there would be a row, and so things went on. Bellew was a hard-drinking fish. He had been in a Cavalry regiment and had retired; he had had money and had spent most of it. Anthony shrewdly suspected him of relations with other women. For months past nothing had been seen or heard of him; it was this, no doubt, this prolonged estrangement and prolonged failure of supplies, which made Danaë talk of the stage. As a girl she had been a good amateur actress; her figure, her appearance were in her favour; she was friends with George Forsyte, who had a share in 'The Athenian,' and had promised to see her started! She might be successful, so Anthony thought; but the idea was most displeasing to him. Luckily Vigil's influence was all against it. But had he any influence with her? Anthony doubted it. As for her brother—Solomon would listen, perhaps shake his head, and in the end say: "Well, old girl, you know best!"

Anthony opened his eyes. By his side, holding out a hand, was Gregory Vigil himself. Tall, with a fresh-coloured face and grey moustache, he had the look of a man who has just drunk two glasses of red wine—sad or dejected, anxious or calculating, he was never without this look; it was as essentially a part of him as his light, long stride, his pleasant high voice, the whispering affectionateness of his manner. His prominent blue-grey eyes, suffused with a moist gleam, seemed to brim with affection, as though he had been long baulked of an overmastering desire to embrace something. And such indeed had been his fate. His life had been singularly pure. In the course of fifty years he had known but one brief period of lapse, one brief period when he had eaten husks with the swine. Out of that short and bitterly-sweet sleep he had suddenly awakened. A deep and painful convulsion, shaking the very roots of his being, had left him at the age of twenty-six with the conviction that he was defiling himself, that he was meant for higher things. And in that cataclysm he suddenly found God, as it were, at his elbow, like a kind but strict Father, guiding him to a loftier state. Through all his after-struggles, painful, sometimes despairing, with a nature sensuous and disposed to love, he had never lost that sense of personal contact and overmastering fortuitous guidance, without which he must so often have yielded to his instincts. And that kind of moist light which shone from his eyes, that almost prophetic faith in which all his actions and words were steeped, were physiologically, no doubt, due to the habitual starvation of his lower nature. He had commenced life as a schoolmaster in one of our largest Public Schools, nor was it till he was thirty-five and had attained therein to a position of conspicuous influence, that he felt called upon to resign his post and devote himself to higher and more important work. The death of a relative about this time, leaving him his own master, afforded him the opportunity for realising a conviction that had long been forcing itself upon him, the conviction that he had no right any longer to keep to himself the purity which he had strug-

gled so desperately to bring into his own life. Whether from
some Norse strain in his ancestry or from the fact of birth in
a seaport town, the sea and such as had to do with the sea had
always possessed a fascination for him. He had travelled as
a young man, had talked to sailors and seen something of
their life—and now that he was free to enter that channel
in which he might do most good in the world, he had felt
himself mysteriously impelled towards endeavouring to
shield and save seamen from the temptation to which, by
the very nature of their lives, more than any other men, they
were exposed. After long and arduous canvassing, in the
course of which he met with indifference, sympathy, and
opposition, he succeeded in founding the "Society for the
Protection of British Seamen in Foreign Ports"—more
shortly known as the S.P.B.S. Probably, though he would
never personally admit it, he was greatly helped in its insti-
tution by the fact that the seamen to be protected were British, and the temptations from which they were to be protected were foreign; be this as it may—the Society, once in-
itiated, was unquestionably successful in saving many a sea-
man for himself; and though its various branches required
Gregory's constant attention, he still found time and energy
to devote to his other neighbours' affairs.

It was in his struggle to launch the Society that he first
came into contact with Anthony Thornworthy, then Chairman of the Mexico and Peru Shipping Co., upon whom he
called one afternoon by appointment at the Company's offices
in Moorgate Street.

Anthony, then in the prime of his capacity, a handsome
man just going grey, eyed his visitor with a keen smile, and
listened courteously to this sanguine nervous young man
with the high and pleasant voice.

"But, come, what's it to me," he said at last, "if a sailor
lets out a little of his vitality at the end of a voyage?" And
with some curiosity he waited for the answer. How would

the young man justify his idea? If this were the scheme of a crank, or a church matter—he would have nothing to do with it!

Gregory had agreeably disappointed him; with a shrewdness for which Anthony gave him full credit, he had kept strictly to the material advantages of his scheme, producing figures which proved incontestably that drink and disease contracted by British seamen at foreign ports were two of the principal reasons why captains of British ships were obliged to enlist so many foreigners amongst their crews. And it was in a cynical admiration of this shrewdness, rather than with any belief in the enterprise, that Anthony promised his support. He took a liking, in fact, for this fresh-coloured, active young fellow who was so thoroughly English. If the young man found it profitable to spend his time in reforming other people, it was nothing to him, Anthony! And when, soon afterwards, he made that provision for his wife and for old age that has been alluded to, it was to Gregory that he paid the compliment of appointing him sole trustee.

This was before Danaë's marriage to Bellew, when she was but seventeen; and Gregory shyly, furtively adoring, had only too happily assented to fulfil a position which promised a permanent connection with her. From her marriage he had suffered silently and loyally; when that marriage assumed the spasmodic character which had marked the last five years, he suffered perhaps still more. With his belief in the sanctity of the marriage tie, it shocked and dismayed him that they should live apart; it shocked and dismayed him still more to find that he dwelt on the fact that she lived apart, with a sort of unholy relief; most of all was he dismayed by the accesses of rage which seized on him when Jaspar Bellew paid her one of his rare visits; and now that these rare visits, even, seemed to have ceased, he lived like a man exhausted, wondering and relieved, after the strange healing of the old intermittent wound, refusing to believe that it would ever break out again. With Anthony he had remained on good terms. One day at dinner, a glass of port in his hand, the old man had thus summed up Gregory's character to his daughter: "A good fellow, but he can't let well alone—must have a finger in the pie." Immovable himself, he did not find this peculiarity disturbing. It amused him. . . .

The two walked together from St. James's Park station towards the pile of buildings in Victoria Street which contained Anthony's flat.

A lift, worked by a man in a short brown livery jacket, with the peculiar pale sad face of those whose lives are passed in watching others going up and down, soon brought them to the fifth floor. Anthony said:

"They pay eighty pounds more on the first floor—twenty pounds for each storey's worth of stink and noise."

With a latchkey attached to a coat button with black silk, where he could come at it without labour, he opened the door. A long corridor was visible, illumined by a single light; on the walls were paintings which nobody at any time of the day could see. A heavy carved oak stand nearly blocking one end, received their hats and coats. A faint odour of good French cooking came to the nostrils. Anthony led the way. A door stopping at length all further promenade, they passed into a room meriting description not so much for the beauty of its furniture as for certain psychological indications. Though now dark outside, the long French window stood wide, and through it could be seen a vista of black roofs, the tops of two trees, the brooding outline of a spire; the booming of distant traffic came in. A great fire, consuming cedar logs, blazed in a hearth constructed for the more modest coal; two high vases of carmine lilies exhaled a penetrating scent, which blended with the fume of the logs. On an open grand piano stood a full-length photograph of a woman; a fur cape that must have slipped from the shoulders of the pianist draped the music stool even to the floor, and scattered sheets of music lay around. The room was profusely lighted. On a large sofa before the fire were seated a woman and a man, who rose as Anthony and Vigil came in.

Danaë Bellew at the age of thirty-six was like nothing so much as a ripe cornfield in the afternoon sun when a breeze blows over it. Her tall form had the swelling billowy look, and her hair the yellow-brown rippling look of corn; her lips and cheeks, which had been too close to the fire, were poppy-red; her silk blouse, of cornflower blue. There was an exuberance of form and colour about her, a prodigality which she seemed to fling at the beholder.

The simile ends. The sun sets, the breeze dies down, and grey quiet settles over the corn. Not so with Danaë; there was no sunset with this woman, at most the filmy veiling of transient clouds, which dimmed in an unconvincing manner her light.

Men were not in the habit of psychologising her; they fell under her sway, or in a few cases retired——finding her too broad for their taste; these called her vulgar. But vulgar was too strong a word, for she had her charm——the truly vulgar have none. To a describer the expression of her face was puzzling. It was neither frank nor disingenuous, yet had the broad naïveté of its overpowering vitality. About the lips was a dash of sensuality, but of a sensuality too quick and sane for vice. Her grey-green eyes were the eyes of a coquette, but her broad low brow and the whole mould of her, that of a woman who could have borne her part in the siege of Lucknow and come through it, while others died. She was so extremely, so irritatingly human, that only once in a way, and by a sort of process of elimination, could there be seen in her the elements of an abstract and classical figure, a sort of Greek breadth and profusion, a natural immorality, now alas! nearly lost.

She came forward with a smile, holding out her hand, and her eyes that took in everything under their lids, glanced from Vigil to the man beside her, who stood with his top hat in his gloved hand, a sardonic smile on his mottled brown face. From his patent-leather boots to a simple sailor-knot tie, her visitor was dressed with that unostentatious modishness which denotes the man to whom Club life has become a necessity. His full eyes, of an undetermined grey, stared at the newcomer, and in that stare was a sort of permanent and secret jeer. This was George Forsyte, second son of Roger Forsyte of Prince's Gardens, who, like his three brothers, Roger and Thomas and Eustace, had been brought up to the profession invented by old Roger—collection of house property. Unlike them, he had not prospered. There was something in his soul above house property; the collection of it had not presented to him the facility for sportsmanlike adventure which his nature demanded. Two or three financial crises had been tided over by old Roger, who, having lived all his life in the faith of his own invention, was loath, at the age of seventy-two, to admit a case of failure. And indeed, since the last crisis, the wheel of fortune seemed to have turned in his son's favour. George now spoke of his condition as 'rosy,' talked of a purchase in Shaftesbury Lane and some property in Epsom as 'A1.' Roger, still a busy man, and at that time particularly absorbed in the acquisition of a block of buildings in Fulham, a neighbourhood just then beginning to be known, had not made himself completely master of all the details of these adventures. Divested of George's peculiar and often witty verbiage, they amounted to a fifth share in 'The Athenian' theatre (until lately in low water), and the whole of a three-year-old, trained by Blacksmith of Epsom. Both—as he phrased it—were 'doing him well.' 'The Termagant,' a piece not wholly unconnected with ladies' legs, was now about entering its second century, and in the then condition of public taste, promised to run for ever. The three-year-old, baptized by George 'The Ambler,' having shown more than a suspicion of form in one or two home trials, had been withdrawn from the public gaze, and supported judiciously, till he stood in the 'Rutlandshire' quotations at 10—1. The commission had been executed by Barney's, than whom no commissioners can be more strongly recommended to owners, for enlisting in a horse's favour the public sympathy. And now that the public was determined to 'have' 'The Ambler' at 10—1 George found himself in the position of one who was able to lay off his bets, some of which were at very nice outside prices, and stand to win the sum of four thousand pounds to nothing. A few more substantial bets against the horse, and he might have made certain of a large stake even should the animal not start. But, a Public School man and a gentleman, his turf morality was sound; he had a sense of good form, and was one of the last to lend himself to anything that would look shady; no idea of pushing the situation further and making himself absolutely certain of gain, by scratching, or forbidding his horse to win, would he for a moment have entertained. Moreover, unlike many men, the idea of a race really appealed to him; his sound nerve, just pleasantly soothed by drink, enjoyed the exhilaration of the 'finish.' Even when beaten there was a sort of enjoyment to be had out of the imperturbability with which he could take the beating, a sense of superiority to men who were not quite so well-bred or so sportsmanlike as himself. And George set much store by his breeding, which he felt in some inscrutable way to be more distinguished than it would have proved, if looked into—(his grandfather had been a master-builder, his great-grandfather a farmer). He had acquaintance with Arthur Badstock, Conny Boyle, and Lord Frittlestoke, amongst others of the racier aristocracy. To find him seated in a lady's drawing-room at the hour commonly consecrated to the cardroom at the Haversnake would to his intimates have

seemed a portent; but the two men who entered were not
of that large class, though Anthony had known him from
his boyhood. Associated in business with the Forsyte family
for many years, a former colleague of old Jolyon Forsyte on
the Board of the Rhyndy Pandy Coalfields, a present colleague of James Forsyte on the Bhang and Sciatic, he had
been accustomed to meet George at Forsyte dinner tables,
and looked upon him with that peculiar half-understanding,
half-distrust, with which the men of the world of one generation look upon the men of the world of the next. There
appeared to him something lacking in the way these young
fellows went to work; something half-hearted about them,
as though they were afraid of the cup they had set to their
lips! Even in their knowingness they seemed to be ashamed
of themselves; they were so cautious, as though they had no
belief in their pleasures, in their lives, in anything! And
deep down, Anthony nourished contempt; it seemed to him
that there was no blood in them. . . .

But putting out his hand he enquired for George's father;
and George, who had an admiration for old Thornworthy
and would speak of him kindly as a 'leery old cock,' answered: "Thanks; the governor's as bright as a star!" And
he opened the door for the old man, who excused himself
with the courtesy which was habitual to him.

George Forsyte came back from the door with a queer,
sardonic smile on his lips. He was looking at Vigil who still
held Danaë's hand. The 'parson,' as he called him, had
from the moment of their first meeting excited George's
amusement; he was quick to perceive in this grey-haired
man with the high colour and the moist, bright eye, a strain
of fanaticism at which he looked askance, as ridiculous, dangerous and lacking in taste. He was the sort of fellow, in
fact, who spoiled sport, and for such—in the language of
the Haversnake—he had 'no use.' And he was the sort of
fellow, too, who hung about a woman and liked to pretend

he was doing her good! Doing her good!—Why couldn't
the fellow say at once that he———. You had only to look at
him! And George's acerbity was increased by consciousness
of Gregory's shrewdness, by the practical side of his character. He, the 'parson,' was wide-awake, it was difficult to
get the laugh of him; he was hot-tempered, too; you had to
mind where you stepped, or he went off like a match! Altogether, perhaps no more unfortunate collection of qualities
could have been found, for George's taste. He felt his dislike returned, but Gregory had not yet shown his hand. His
dealings with men and things as Secretary of the S.P.B.S.
had steeled and toughened the surface of a sensitive but
naturally reserved nature. When he met George at Danaë
Bellew's (the two men were constant callers) he preserved
towards him an interested, scrutinising, suave demeanour,
which afforded George but small scope for taking a rise out
of him; and our Forsyte could not help feeling admiration
for the way the fellow kept his end up. It came home to him
now with strange vividness that he was fighting, if not
against Vigil himself, against his influence, for the possession
of this woman. Yet he was not seriously alarmed, for, like
her own father, he felt that she with whom he was in love
was not really influenced by anyone. It was her great attraction. She was not possessed of any striking eccentricity or
originality of mind which would have been no attraction to
George, who rightly considered originality subversive of
good taste; she was not that hard-mouthed thing, a 'strong-
minded woman'; it was something in her quite different,
deeper. George had not explained it to himself; he was no
eloquent psychologist. But she seemed to swim on the top of
things, to 'bob up' serenely to-morrow, however down in the
depths she might be to-day. She was always well, and looked
beautiful, however she complained (as she not infrequently
did) of life's treatment. And it was by instinct, by no rea-
soned conclusions, that he knew nothing could really turn

her, for nothing—such was her vitality—could really touch
her. In his dumb and peculiar philosophy, being neither a
bad-hearted nor a stupid man, he found it comforting to
feel that, whatever the outcome of this passion which he no
longer attempted to disguise from himself, she would not
really suffer, however he might himself come off. And at
times he felt sorry for the 'parson,' handicapped as he was
by his principles. There were moments when he felt himself winning. More generally, he smothered with difficulty,
under his sardonic grin, jealousy at that caressing, deferen-
tial manner she always displayed in Vigil's presence. And he
would wonder what it was she expected to get out of the fellow, or whether it was merely her woman's whim to keep
in his good graces. But dumb was his wonder, dumb his
speculation, for he had come to have for her the sort of
longing he had believed himself to have outgrown—a longing that made him seek solitary nooks at the Haversnake,
made him by turns indifferent to, and passionately impa-
tient of, its cooking, a longing that brought at times a worn
look to his fleshy face. However, hedonistic the order of his
life, a man cannot deny his blood; and to George, born and
bred to commercialism, this passion for a married woman,
coming not in his first youth, was charged with the countless
doubts and fears that hover around passion in a fundamentally commercial mind. It set the scheme of things awry,
fogged values which had seemed as clear as summer day-
light. Sleeping and waking, he was haunted by the nightmare of that question: Was it worth it?—that he should be
thus deprived of his natural liking for the gossip of his
fellows, for long hours of 'poker,' and whist, and billiards;
deprived of aspirations which for years had been the loftiest
in his soul; deprived of the philosophy that to be out in the
air all day, to dine well, drinking a special brand of Pol
Roger, and now and then thereafter to enjoy the society of
women, was the highest happiness a man could hope for.

Was worth it—to look forward to the Divorce Court and perjury as a co-respondent; or alternatively, an existence with a woman you were tired of, on the fringe of Society? Was it worth it—with the governor so strait-laced and the chance of his cutting you off with a shilling? Was it worth it—to drag round day after day, perspiring lest you should find her out, and as often as not come on that d——d parson seated there? Was it worth it—for a woman that you couldn't make out, that had something in her that beat you altogether; who enjoyed things too much, too unreflectingly, or was down, down in the depths? Was it worth it?—— George's reason told him 'No.' He was putting his money on the wrong horse, and with all his might he tried to hedge his bets; but secretly he felt that he could not. And with his profound commercial morality, typical of his breed and class, believing that a man should not spend himself without reward, he really understood the 'parson' with his ascetic morals better than he understood the woman he loved. Vigil expected to get something for his abstinence, no doubt; if not in this world, then in the next. But Danaë went her way without thinking of the future; it was his belief that she had no morals.

And seeing from her manner that Vigil was now to have his innings he came forward and held out his hand.

"Well, I'll be toddling," he said. "You won't forget the 24th," and took his way downstairs.

CHAPTER III

BUT George, in estimating the character of the man he left behind him in Danaë's drawing-room, had, as is ever the case, done but half the sum.

True, Gregory looked for recompense from that fatherly figure at his side, but this with him was not the whole story. To have gone on, assured of his own benefit, without bringing that benefit to others, was a tasteless business, and life—thus—one long egg without salt. In assisting the salvation of others was he predestined to satisfy his competitive and fighting spirit, inherited from his Norse and Anglo-Saxon ancestors and the centuries of Christianity in which they had been brought up. Neither ill-naturedly nor unnaturally, he did not like other men to enjoy pleasures which he felt were not beneficial to himself. The process in his mind was too subtle for the proverb: 'Sour grapes'—a proverb never kindly used in a universe where each man, woman or child is to that man, woman or child the most important thing in all the world. A true Englishman, there was but little of the impersonal in his character. Fate, or more precisely the trend of his own nature, had ruled that he should not enter that Church for which he had been destined. Through the earlier stages of preparation at College he had passed to the later reading necessary to enable him at the age of twenty-three to point out the true path of life to such as, for double that time, had been stumbling about to find it. And this later reading had brought seriously to his notice the doctrine of the resurrection of the body; for some inscrutable reason he began to think about this doctrine, and ultimately decided that he could not believe it. He had much of the spirit that conforms to attain its end, and if left to himself it is possible that Gregory would have come to see that he was justified in placing on this doctrine such an interpretation of his own as would meet the difficulty. But it so happened that at this crisis he became acquainted with a young man in Holy Orders who withstood him in argument throughout a College evening, endeavouring to force on him a literary acceptation. Gregory was aroused. From that day he felt it his duty to renounce his intention of entering the Church. Nothing in after life had modified this conviction, or caused him to regret the decision to which he had come; in every other respect he remained a true Christian, English and individualistic to the core. He held the near and personal conception of the Deity, characteristic of men who do most good in the world. God to him was an incarnation of all the best points and qualities that he recognised in himself and the most admirable people that he met and read of, a sort of idealised Brown, Smith, and Robinson—it is doubtful if he admitted Jones, a Welshman and deeply imbued with the Celtic temperament. This personal conception of the Deity gave him a clarity and directness of view over his own and his neighbour's duties, such as would otherwise have been lacking, and inspired in him a power of convinced and ecstatic vision. Nothing could be doubtful, submitted to and judged by so definite a personality as his God; all the struggles and fears of his man's heart he felt must be unreal and shadowy; at bottom all was certain and arranged. It surprised and annoyed him that he suffered, but this suffering made him tolerant of the sufferings of others, up to a point not exceeding that which his nature told him was reasonable, and his religion showed him to be lawful. Yet, in his compassion, strange to say, there was no real certainty; it was ill prophesying; for, as in his religion he was personal, so in human matters was he very personal, and liable to be swayed by the affections. He found, for instance, Mrs. Dance— the wife of the dissolute Dance, a lady for whom he had no real liking—unintelligibly weak to suffer the desertion of her husband, and the matter left him cold; while in Danaë's case his blood boiled at the thought of that fellow Bellew. He longed to mount, and ride upon him, to call him to appreciate his wife at her proper worth or take the consequences. And he was quite capable, in the generosity of his homage, of overlooking any other side there might be to the case. It is true that Danaë did not give him much chance of seeing any other side; she had been so used to his sympathy and admiration from girlhood that it had become essential to her. She was sincere to her moods, and to Gregory her mood was always soft, always the most subdued and appealing mood of which her exuberant vitality was capable. Her softness and appeal were not deliberate; originally inspired by his own deference, it had become a habit. Her greatest difficulty, now and always, was financial, yet in Gregory she had established a fixed belief that this was only incidental to her matrimonial position. In fact, it went deeper. From the day when she first had money in her pinafore, she had never been out of debt; it was a constitutional matter, occasioning other people more suffering than herself. Those who heard her lament her unfortunate position were ever touched to the heart; strangely moved, their hands went mechanically to their pockets. Danaë herself was not moved; her lament was too chronic. Nor was it for the sake of getting money from people that she made her moan; it was more an unconscious luxuriating in the mood of the moment, an unconscious indulgence that had incidentally good effects. Continually, remorselessly immersed in monetary troubles and transactions, she had perhaps the only truly uncommercial disposition of her time. She owned, in fact, her father's full-blooded fidelity to his sensations, and from her Welsh mother derived that which some people called her unreliability. She was happy, she was often miserable—she enjoyed being both; she enjoyed being as happy as she could, she enjoyed being as miserable as she could; and the future played no real part in her life! Other people calculated, she made, therefore, a point of calculating, too; her conversation to Gregory was frequently full of calculations, and she quite enjoyed them; they meant nothing, for, in fact, she was quite incapable of reckoning. The cup was at her lips all the time, and all the time she was drinking. She had been born on Valentine's Day, with a little cloud of golden fluff on her head; and Anthony, with whom the birth synchronised with a piece of commercial good fortune, in vague recollections of Ovid, suggested the name of Danaë. And in gratitude for recollection of their existence in forgetful days, the Pagan gods had visited Danaë in some sort.

It is to her first lover, George's cousin, young Jolyon Forsyte—the only, and now-reinstated son of old Jolyon Forsyte—that we owe the recognition of this fact. The painter (his medium was water-colour) who now lived with his father, his second wife, and their two children in the house at Robin Hill, met his old flame again, for the first time twenty years after the rupture of their engagement.

"You are," he said, "the best Pagan I've ever seen, and your brother Solomon's the best Christian"—a diagnosis the truth of which suffers in reflecting that, as a matter of common knowledge, Solomon never went to church and held almost Socialistic views.

Danaë had turned her grey-green eyes on young Jolyon's lean figure, and lean, long face with its drooping moustache and grizzled hair, and answered:

"You always were nasty to me!" but, suddenly perceiving that he had intended a compliment, she gave him a slow, sweet, side-long smile; she attached, in fact, but hazy meanings to such words as 'Pagan.'

Young Jolyon raised his brows. "Was I? I had thought——"

She laughed her soft laugh, gave him another look, and dropped her eyes.

But young Jolyon had effected a permanent cure—he returned not to his first love; Danaë at sixteen and Danaë at thirty-six were not the same; the dew had dried off the petals of the rose, and it was the dew that had brought him fluttering to drink. He had inherited philosophy, had acquired the ironical eye. She was nothing now to him but a specimen of horticulture. The rose was full-blown; the lines too rounded, the perfume too intoxicating; nor did the love experiences of his life tend to encourage experiment. Yet like a connoisseur, inhaling the cigar of his own past, he came often to spend an hour in her society, praising Fortune gently that she had jilted him, and from her little daughter Thyme catching strange hints of the Danaë of his youth. The Danaë of his youth, before Vigil had known her, or Jaspar Bellew, or his cousin George! The girl with the unimaginably quick, gay eyes, and clear voice, insatiable by dance, song, or laughter, insatiable of the gaze of men; insatiable of life, as life itself. At fifteen she had plucked the hearts out of men by the score, not cruelly, but all in the day's work; had wished them all well when she did so, and would have rewarded them, no doubt, had it but been practicable. He remembered begging to be allowed to pay her little bills, remembered her gay refusal; and how, when by sheepish devices he managed to pay them after all, she had only threatened him with her finger and laughed again. The girl who, a fortnight after telling him in secrecy that she would be his wife, went out riding for a whole day with another man, and to his reproaches, returned the answer: "I said—some day, Jo. Don't you want me to enjoy myself?"

And, seeming to find that he did not, he had broken away with heart badly torn; besides himself, she was engaged at that time to one other man at least.

Occupied with the ill-advised marriage into which reaction at once plunged him, and the great passion for another woman which not unnaturally followed, he had but vaguely remarked Danaë's course. Her brother Solomon was the only one of his friends of those days with whom, after his elopement, he had kept up. He too would no doubt have gone by the board, for, though there had been no public scandal, young Jolyon had had a delicacy about old friends—had he not run across him one evening on his way back from the Temple.

Solomon was swinging his tall and bulky form along the Embankment, his head thrown well back, stick rotating, beaming at the world through the pince-nez on his short, straight, ingenuous nose—he had just left Oxford, and perhaps at no subsequent period of his career was he older than at this time. Unendowed with any elegance whatever, everyone accused him of being a gentleman; for, though his presence was conspicuous, he was never conscious of it; a simple bonhomie made him everywhere at home. Seeing young Jolyon, his senior by some six or seven years, and whom he knew to be in a scrape, he at once bore down upon him.

"Hullo, young Jo!" he said.

Young Jolyon, compressing his lips, looked up in Solomon's face, and answered defiantly between his teeth:

"Hullo, old Sol!"

But they continued their way together.

In no words could young Jolyon have done justice to the restfulness of that walk. It was the first time since his episode that he found himself in company with a human being who, knowing all the facts, neither ignored them nor made anything of them, nor seemed in the least conscious that there was anything to make. His stubborn will, which had never ceased painfully telling him that he was in the right, suddenly went to sleep. This was Solomon's charm; he was an anodyne whom people sought, as people seek in travel

some sane landscape to soothe their strung-up nerves, on its
large, cheerful, unconscious suavity. From time to time
Solomon had supplied casual information concerning his
sister. Danaë was married—a good enough match—Bellew
a very decent chap if you took him the right way; a desperate
character—over this description Solomon would smile. He
liked that about Bellew; it was attractive—he himself was
not a desperate character. Two children were born—"jolly
little beggars"—(no boy at Meryon's school could hold a
candle to him for sheer, cool-blooded mischief). A bit of a
row?—Yes—they thought it better to be each on their
own—he expected it probably was! Money was—h'm—
scarce—the poor old girl was always hard up. He had talked
to Bellew; there was a good deal to be said for him. He'd
been unlucky; a fellow like that was never quite tame. "I
talked to him seriously."

Young Jolyon smiled.

"And what did you say?"

Solomon beamed slowly.

"I told him," he said, "not to be a silly ass. He doesn't
mean any harm. It's his way."

"They talk at the Club about D. T."

Over Solomon's face came a certain gravity.

"Yes," he said; "but very mild. I sat up with him."

"Did you tell your sister?"

Solomon's eyes widened behind their pince-nez; he looked
surprised.

"No," he said, "no. It was quite a chance that I was
there."

Young Jolyon browsed on the remark.

This was Solomon all over, who seemed to pass through
life steeped in a sort of Arabian hospitality. In Solomon's
place he too would have concealed the fact from Danaë;
not from an instinct of hospitality but from a distrust of the
lady, founded partly on experience and partly in the con-

sciousness that he did not understand her. And, far more
subtle than his cousin George, young Jolyon found his
ignorance of her a fertile source of speculation.

To a man like Gregory Vigil, however, Danaë Bellew
was as clear as the colour of her hair. She incarnated for
him all that was adorable in woman, the more so that it had
become a superstition with him that she was his good angel,
keeping him from himself, and that he was hers, performing
for her the same function. In his relations with her he kept
this ever in view. It is doubtful in fact whether he could
safely have had relations with a woman without the aid
of this superstition. He had never married, because of her;
it would have seemed to him a sacrilege. . . .

And now that he was alone with her in this drawing-
room, scented with the perfume of those lilies given by another man, he walked up and down like some caged animal, with his long, soft stride and his eyes sometimes far off,
sometimes fixed upon her lustrously.

"I don't like him—I shall never like him. He's a man
of the world, he's a gambler, he's a ——" He checked himself; the word sensualist was not fitted for her ears! "He
lives to enjoy——"

Danaë laughed; her laugh had mellowed; it was soft,
full, mechanical, the laugh of a woman who had found it
useful, attractive, necessary.

"Poor George!" she murmured; "but he's going to help
me."

Gregory halted as though the words had pierced him like
an arrow; he passed his hand over his eyes, and his forehead
flushed.

"It makes me sick," he said, "to think of you on the
stage."

She shrugged her shoulders. "What would you have?"
Then, with a sort of slow passion, as though the announcement were new, and strange, and terrible, she burst out:

"I'm in debt!"

He began his walk again. As a man of business, accustomed to deal shrewdly enough with the moneys of a Public Society, the announcement might well have startled him. It did not, however, for he had heard it any time these twenty years, and it was perhaps the fact that he was the only man she knew who had never met the announcement by lending her money, that inspired in Danaë the respect she undoubtedly had for him, the deeply rooted desire to keep him at her call. By instinct he had never lent her money, and also because the idea of it would have sullied his high conception of her. Often in his rooms, in a Westminster side-street, clad in the underwear peculiar to him, going through the muscular exercises he had himself invented, he turned over and over anxiously that question: "Shall I lend her money?" It is not too much to say that he would have gone into the City, sold out the major portion of his stocks, and poured the proceeds into her lap without a sigh. But to what end? He would not have been in the position he was, Honorary Secretary of the S.P.B.S., had he not possessed both shrewdness and common sense, qualities almost invariably found in the British character, and especially among that large minority who do good to others. To what end? The money would go; her position would remain what it was—that position which was at the root of the evil; it would only weaken his own resources and his power of doing her good. And he would stand before the glass, staring with blank eyes at the muscles of his long figure, now going a little slack. . . .

He gave her no answer, but asked:

"What is it he wants you to do on the 24th?"

Danaë made a soft movement of the arm. "Come, do sit down," she said, "here by me. You make me nervous."

Gregory took his seat on the sofa by her side. His high colour deepened, his eyes were lowered; a trembling had seized his limbs, the trembling of a man faint with hunger. And Danaë, soft, with her hair coiled like golden snakes down her gracious head to her gracious neck, her limbs stretched luxurious in their silken covering, looked at him sidelong, with a matter-of-fact compassion. If he had leaned forward and seized her in his arms she would not have resisted. Poor fellow, he deserved all he could get! But she did not want him to. She had no time to think about such things. Besides, there was George, poor old George, to whom, if to anyone—— And she looked at Gregory and pitied him, woman-like, for taking things so hard, indulgent as to an angel. But Gregory had that other profoundly British quality; at the bottom of his heart there was a secret reserve of strength, a sort of permanent balance at his moral Bank. Things might hurt, things might go very hard—he could stand the racket. And he looked up at her, and asked again:

"What is it he wanted you to do on the 24th?"

"The 24th? Oh! there is a dance at some people's in Cambridgeshire. Will you come too? I will get you an invitation."

Gregory asked: "Will Forsyte be there?"

Danaë answered: "I believe he is going down for some shooting. You had better come, Gregory."

She knew that he would not come. With a sigh he answered that his dancing days were over. In truth, he had never had any but with her—she knew this, too. In her large, easy heart she almost loved him for it.

And she said: "I don't know where I shall get the money for a dress!"

She said it from habit, and without intention; to her astonishment he answered:

"I will send you one."

She seized his hand: "Will you? That will be lovely. I will be sure and wear it in memory of you."

He took his hand gently from her, and got up to go.

"I will certainly send it," he said, and went away.

In the hall of the Mansions a man passed him, coming in, who nodded, and asked:

"Mrs. Bellew at home?"

Gregory turned sharply, like a dog that can suffer none to approach its mistress unchallenged.

"Oh! it's you," he said. "Yes, she's at home, but it's rather late."

Young Jolyon Forsyte smiled.

"It's the children I'm after," he said. "Good night!" and he passed on into the lift.

Gregory ran his hand through his fine grey hair, which was always a little long and bushy; he knew not what to make of this man who seemed to have the power of approaching the goddess with an impunity that he could not but suspect, and resent.

CHAPTER IV

DANAË, when he had gone, experienced a momentary sensation of discomfort. A dress? Such a funny thing to propose—but dear old Gregory was always funny. And her moral uneasiness passed—that sensation such as a cat must feel, turned for a moment out of some habitual nook, the sensation of ruffled fur, of what was not quite usual, against her back.

She had thought it unnecessary to tell him that the invitation had been procured by George, that the party was arranged for the Newmarket Autumn Meeting, at which George's horse 'The Ambler,' on whom she stood, in George's book, to win four hundred pounds to nothing, was running for the 'Rutlandshire.' What use to tell such things to a man of Gregory's known views? And rising from the sofa, she went to the door and called: "Thyme!"

A young girl, all cheeks and legs, but legs that showed the beginnings of beauty, came flying down the passage, to transfix her mother with the points of her elbows and chin and knees.

Danaë felt that her children were 'awful,' but she enjoyed them when she had time; and, if she scolded them it was in a voice so cheerful, so redolent of good red blood, that it could not but raise their spirits.

"Where," she said, "is that awful boy?"

Thyme's grey eyes, niched in between brow-bones and the roundness of her cheeks, not large but deep-set and wide with candour, became like moons; her face, all apple-blossom, with its dimpled pointed chin, deepened to red; the pigtail of fair hair hanging over one thin shoulder, quivered.

"Oh! Mother—he's a pig!"

"Of course he's a pig; all boys are pigs. Now come—what's he doing?"

Thyme answered in a strangled voice: "He's melted Susan; he's sucking her with a straw."

"What Susan?"

"Uncle Solomon's."

Solomon had given her a doll, exquisitely made of French sugar by Buster's of Piccadilly. He had said: "There's apricot jam in the middle."

But Thyme, disregardful, had loved her as a child, had cherished and dressed her for weeks, giving her all those little advantages of clothing and underclothing which disguise from men's eyes the secret weaknesses and beauties of the women they love. She had married her to Mr. Tims, an old dandy in a red shirt, white trousers, and a Homburg hat, a man admirably adapted (out of wood) to protect her from the world.

"Oh! Mother, he *is* such a pig! I've kicked his shins, and he just goes on sucking. He's a beast!"

The tragedy was too deep for tears.

Danaë laughed; checked herself and said: "The wretch! Let go, you bony child! Go and send that boy to me!"

When Meryon came she received him severely. He was a moon-faced boy with a sort of fresh, angelic innocence in his blue eyes and on his somewhat sticky mouth.

"Well, what can you expect, Mother?" he said. "The beastly thing annoyed me, always about, like that! She's such an idiot, that girl; doing her best to spoil it, dressing it up. I offered to let her suck, too; we might have had it ages ago; it's a wonder there's any flavour left!"

"Cannibal—can-ni-bal bo-oy!"

"You hear that?" said Meryon. "She's always at me! She gives me no peace. I tell you what it is, Mother; she's a cat! Is Grampus in?"

Danaë answered: "Grampus indeed? I'll grampus you!

Go to your room and stay there till supper!" and, turning away, she sank down on the sofa and sighed.

"Ah!" she thought. "Lonely and miserable—no one to help me—the world against me—and nothing but debts—debts—debts!" Again she sighed.

And at this second sigh Meryon, knowing himself forgotten, stole out on tiptoe and entered the dining-room.

There, on a crimson damask sofa, sat Anthony asleep. Of Meryon's composition reverence had no part, but in the immovability of the old man something ever fascinated his grandson, and he stood still, to look.

No boy of thirteen is an artist, still less is he that species of analytical chemist who has lately taken the artist's place, and Meryon could not express, even to himself, the impression made by that old, round-limbed, short-necked figure, by the shining red of those cheeks, the shining silver of that forehead and beard, the peculiar sough of the air escaping between the white-fringed lips. This was a sight he could see any day of the week from six to seven, and it never failed to fascinate. Asleep or awake, Anthony produced in his grandson a state of inaction. And, ambushed from habit behind an armchair, he watched those slumbers, as in some old picture a young Faun watches Silenus asleep, red-faced and silver-haired, from behind a tree. Nor was the background unlike that Pagan mythology, for Anthony had brought to this somewhat temporary perch much old English furniture, the relics of Squire Baldwin Thornworthy's ancestral mansion 'up to Bovey'; and with the old English furniture something of the atmosphere which belonged to the hard-riding, port-drinking, free-loving days of the Squire, when the country was orthodox and Christian to a man, in the loyal belief that the British temperament was the ideal, original soil for Christian seed, and good hard hitting in Commerce, camp, and Church, the first teaching of Christ. Comparatively few were left now, and those nearly all on the Stock Exchange, who, like Anthony—orthodox Churchmen—disputing nothing, passed the purely Pagan lives of that older and more Christian epoch. Comparatively few, now that the country laboured in the early—and as yet unconscious—throes of an attempt to disgorge a religion which had never suited it, but lain undigested, contributing little if any nourishment to the system, and against whose fundamental flavour every fibre of the national stomach had ever revolted.

Such reflections passed through the mind of young Jolyon Forsyte, who, ushered in five minutes before by a maid ignorant of Anthony's presence, sat cross-kneed and quiet in a dark corner. With his eyes on Meryon crouched behind a chair—"an amazing thing," he thought, "that we've never found out that this struggle to assimilate a religion that does not suit us is responsible for all our world-renowned hypocrisy."

Through the silence of the room rumbled the long-drawn sobbing breath, as of the soul returning to the body, which preceded Anthony's awakening. Jolyon saw the boy Meryon steal to the sideboard, make a hasty collection, and gain the door, paying with thumb and nose a cheerful tribute to some presiding genius. And he mused: "That boy is right. Instead of curling his tail and whining, when Fortune smiles, for fear she should change her mind (as we do, and call it gratitude), he cocks a snook. The boy is right."

The maid entered, and summoned him away.

He never approached Danaë without a mechanical shiver, reflex action, no doubt, from the emotions of long ago; and never without a slight but not unkindly smile.

She received him to-day with a look faintly arch, remotely, unconsciously mocking, as to a man who had loved her and not won her, and now loved her no longer.

On hearing from the maid that he was there her violent

dejection had vanished; it was succeeded by a gentle sensation of self-pity, and that soft, sad enticement betrayed itself in the slow languor of her limbs, in the expression of the eyes she turned on him.

And young Jolyon, over whom she now had no power, amused himself with observing the unconscious actress within her; had she been aware of her manner, she could never have done it so well.

He was not of the sounder order of citizens who require the whole world to conform to their tastes; he had rather a tendency to impersonally observe himself and others, which, in conjunction with a peculiar point of view and the remains of an immoral reputation clinging to him, as camphor clings to clothes, caused many to look on him askance.

And Danaë, who by instinct felt that impartial eye upon her, was ever armoured, in his presence, in a silken melancholy.

"I have come begging," he said. "Let me take the children down to Robin Hill. Jolly and Holly are pining for them. There never were four youngsters with more dissimilar temperaments; they're bound to get on. And if you like to run down at any time yourself, my wife will be delighted to make your acquaintance."

A smile played in the folds of his cheeks, and he added: "You'll have the Dad to——" the expression 'flirt with' seemed vulgar, and he stopped.

"Your father is a splendid man," she said; "if you had been he I should never——"

Young Jolyon interrupted her humbly: "Exactly: that I know!"

Danaë lay back in her chair, her face screened from him by the fire-fan in her hand.

"Do you ever see your Uncle Roger?" she asked.

"No," replied young Jolyon.

"Then you don't know your cousins, I suppose; one of them comes to see me. Do you know him—George?"

Young Jolyon answered: Yes—he had met George at Solomon's. And he watched her, slowly fanning her face. One or two hints, his old experience of her, and his insight into men of George's calibre, enabled him to read her like a book. He saw that she wanted to talk to him on this subject, but was afraid. 'How will she wrap it up?' he thought.

"I shall get Solomon to tell him he ought not to give me things. He gave me those lilies," and her eyes seemed to say: 'You never give me anything, now.' "He ought not to spend his money on me. He's not a rich man, is he?"

"Constitutionally, no."

"I don't know what you mean by that; I never know what you mean by things; you're so—so—shadowy."

Indeed, he had a shadowy look; like a man who, not content with living on the income, has dipped into the capital of his emotions; his eye was by turns introspective and enquiring; his cheeks hollow; his face a little ravaged, but withal amiable, and with its pinch of humour.

"George is *not*; at all events," he said. "He's a good fellow, I believe." He habitually spoke well of his individual neighbours, and in the bulk despised them, as those do who have been through trouble.

"He's not her lover, yet," he thought.

She said softly, as though to herself; "Well, I shan't let him come here and waste his time on me; my position is hopeless——"

"But he will be, soon," thought young Jolyon, and he made his request again. "Then you will let me take the children? I particularly want Thyme."

Danaë murmured abstractedly: "They are perfectly awful. You say °George is a good fellow (I call him George). He's not a bit like you. Gregory doesn't like him.

Is he very—fast?" She laughed the laugh of a woman who asks such a question.

Young Jolyon thought: "If I say 'No' it will not please her any more than if I say 'Yes'."

Danaë went on: "I wonder what Jaspar would say. Gregory says I oughtn't to see so much of George—you see I tell you everything. Poor Gregory!"

She stopped, and shading her face, leaned forward, staring at the hearth; the rich gleams flamed round her glowing cheeks and ripe hair, suffused and made her shine with soft fire, like a ruby.

Bellew—George! It was all comedy; but this—Gregory —was very far from being comedy! He had never met the man Vigil without a queer sensation as if someone had put a hand at the back of his neck, and tried softly to push him forward. Fate had not been kind, indeed, bringing up at their first meeting, by unfortunate chance, a matrimonial incident then under treatment in the daily papers. Vigil had expressed his views to Solomon: People—he thought—were not entitled to take the law into their own hands.

This was precisely, of course, what young Jolyon had done. He listened with a doubtful smile, and said nothing. Never since had he felt at ease in Vigil's presence, possessed by a secret irritation that seemed to be fermenting in the base of his temperament. He felt, in fact, that if he saw too much of him, this man would want him to do and see things according to the Vigil way. And, fundamentally peaceful, but fundamentally perverse, young Jolyon could not bear this feeling, which threatened both his peace and his perversity. At times, it gave him quite an uncanny turn. Through his sensations he divined the essence of Vigil's nature, perceived that he was mysteriously, tragically bound from birth to death to see that others did and thought like himself.

And, looking at Danaë, quite a shiver of pity went through young Jolyon, for a man whom he really liked, but could not sit in the same room with. A quaint piece of irony, it seemed, that Vigil should have fixed his affections on this woman, of all others! And he looked at her with interest, with a faint aversion, as a man might look at a jewel full of soft light, that nothing can scratch or change.

It would have pleased him to paint her thus, glowing with colour, a smile on her lips. To an artist (though his medium was water-colour and Danaë's personality demanded oils) she could not fail to be interesting, a piece of Nature's prodigality; and now that the turn of the wheel had removed from young Jolyon the necessity of making money by his pictures, he found a ready market for them, and his devotion to the pursuit had increased by leaps and bounds.

"I met Vigil in the hall," he said. "He thought it a little late for me to be coming up; and so———"

He rose, and held out his hand.

Danaë did not move. "But you must stay to dinner," she said. "Solomon is coming."

At half-past seven they sat down to dinner. Solomon was in dress clothes and wore a white waistcoat; he maintained the usages of Society in the teeth of Radical principles, from a certain large habitual neglect of externals.

At the head of the table sat Anthony in his black velvet jacket.

It is ever from their manner of eating that one divines the true essence of souls; which is but just, seeing that without eating they would soon be past psychology. When Anthony ate, he employed great methods. One knew him at once for a man of courage, of stubborn tenacity, of a shrewd if not cynical judgment. As he was very feeble, he protected his chest with his napkin; but by negative signs, by the omission of certain trenchant tricks, such as the con-

sumption of peas off the end of a knife, he was seen to be
a man of breeding and fashion. He partook largely of
every dish, even when, as often, fidelity to his sensations
had caused him to pronounce them unfit to touch. Wine,
sauces, cigars, and tea, he preferred them all with character. He found no pleasure in tea unless it was black; he
favoured port, maintaining throughout life that it was the
true after-wine to champagne, but he required from it the
'old boot' flavour. Sauces of fine but devastating temperament he took with everything—game-birds alone excepted,
which he ate high and untamed, in their own juices. Cigars
he smoked to their very end, sucking them slowly through
a meerschaum holder. In entertainment he gave of the
best, with Roman splendour causing creatures to be brought
from long distances, and vegetable substances to be cooked
in peculiar ways. To recoil before difficulty was foreign to
his temperament; and strawberries grew for him in January. The longest and happiest hours of his old age were
passed with a fork in his hand. In vain men spoke of his
appetite, envied him his gourmetic tastes, his Norse-like
stomach—it was all one to Anthony. Not for nothing was
he a Stoic.

Opposite him Solomon, like many large young men, ate
but delicately; his size did not seem to depend on sus-
tenance, but rather on his charitable and airy optimism.

Facing young Jolyon sat Danaë, a smile on her face,
and her shoulders gleaming through the openwork of her
loose dinner jacket. And father, brother, and sister seemed
to be giving a sort of show of large and solid red and
white before the lean, shadowy young Jolyon with his thin,
brownish face, and the straitness of his close black coat.

"A strange thing," he said, "this process of eating! Has
it ever struck you, Solomon, what a weird business it is, this
sticking our forks into portions of animals and plants and
lifting them up, making a fissure in our heads and putting

them in? I was dining with my wife at a restaurant the other day, and just as I was lifting up a piece of sweet-bread it came on me so strongly that I put it down again."

Anthony's voice was heard. "Hope you got over it!"

Young Jolyon smiled:

"I maintain that it's the strangest thing in life—that we should have to cut off little bits of pigs and sheep, and absorb them, in order to enable us to contemplate God and the differential calculus."

Danaë said with a laugh: "My dear boy, how do you manage to think of such things? I should never have thought of anything so ridiculous!"

Young Jolyon answered: "But we're not all such splendid Pagans as you."

She stretched herself, raised her glass, and said: "Well, I don't in the least know what you mean."

Solomon chuckled.

"For instance," went on young Jolyon, "if you walk up and down in the evening, at a foreign watering-place, you see glass-fronted restaurants, a lot of little tables, with men, or a man and a woman sitting opposite each other, opening their mouths at intervals and popping little things in, talk-ing all the time about love, or the nicest little shades of Art, or the most rarefied ethics and abstractions. It's too funny for anything."

Anthony stopped eating, and looked fixedly at young Jolyon with his shrewd little deep-set eyes, from which there was projected a sort of infinite understanding.

Solomon said smilingly: "What surprises me, Jo, about those places is, how brutal it must be for the poor starving devils in the streets."

Young Jolyon answered: "Yes, that's interesting, too; such a complete parade could only happen in a Christian country."

"How do you mean?"

Young Jolyon hesitated a moment, looked at Anthony, and said: "No one in this country, I suppose, would deny that the further West you go the more Christian is the country."

"Well?"

"Nor that the further East you go the less sense there is of social order, the less respect for property and distinctions founded on property——"

Again Solomon said: "Well?"

"Such parades are all of a piece with property."

Above a piece of partridge Anthony shot a quizzical glance at his son.

Solomon seemed to reflect: "I should have thought, all the same," he said, "that, take us all round, we English were, at all events, very good Christians."

"The boys at our Public Schools," answered young Jolyon, "speak Latin with such an English accent that not a Roman can be found to understand them."

● Solomon, throwing his large body back in his chair, and beaming still, said: "You're such a sceptic, Jo."

In the silence that followed, Danaë yawned.

"Danaë is bored," said young Jolyon, and in the midst of a second silence a prolonged sigh was heard, such as Nature will sometimes heave out of stillness, as though a strange satisfaction were escaping her—Anthony was drinking.

"How about our reforming spirit?"

Solomon answered: "Well, wasn't Christ a reformer?"

"You know the story of Miss A, the district visitor, elderly and plain, who went to visit Miss B, Irish and red of hair. 'And what can I do for you, Miss B?' 'Sure, ye can write a letter for me, to me son.' 'Your son, Miss B? —but I thought—I thought——' 'Oh! I'd have ye to know, Miss A, that O'*ve* not been entoirely neglected!' Miss A was neither offended, nor did she write the letter;

she made up her mind at once to make a new woman of Miss B."

Danaë laughed. "You oughtn't to tell such naughty stories!"

Anthony's whispering voice was heard from the end of the table: "That's one for Vigil!"

Young Jolyon smiled: "Yes, sir; for a woman of her principles Miss A has been remarkably prolific."

And Solomon, as though speaking to himself, murmured:

"H'm! Christ would have written the letter."

Young Jolyon laid down his knife and fork, turned his face, with its parallel folds, towards Solomon, and, taking a drooping end of moustache in either hand, said:

"Do you really imagine, Sol, that we who never sit down under an affront, whose chief boast is that we can make our own and keep our own, and give as good as we get; whose clergy are the first to insist on the punishment of offenders, and on the conformity of all the world to this point of view——do you imagine we can seriously be considered Christians? No, my boy, we are peculiarly in the spiritual condition of the society at whom Christ preached, and if he appeared again amongst us we should crucify him, with of course those modern refinements that have resulted, not from his teaching, but from scientific inventions and discoveries. I ask you, who is more unpopular at the present day than the 'piece at any price'——never-say-a-word-for-himself——man? We're not Christians a bit; we're humbugs; and only humbugs in words. At heart we're more Pagan than any other people but the Americans."

He paused, his eyes on Danaë's rich ripe figure. Her shoulders and bosom heaved lazily. She said: "You're always calling me a Pagan. I haven't the least idea what you mean!" And as she sighed, a delicious fragrance was wafted to young Jolyon. He turned to Anthony and said: *"You* don't agree with me, sir, I suppose?"

But Anthony nodded at his son, as though to say: "Don't mind me; crack that nut!"

Solomon no longer smiled. The seriousness of his face betrayed the unwonted seriousness of his meditation.

"I don't altogether agree with you, Jo," he said; "I'm always astonished at the number of people who are prepared to sacrifice everything to their convictions. What do you say to that?"

"Three things. First, the *proportionate* number is not large. Second, it is not so much an evidence of Christianity as of fanaticism, which of course is part but not the whole of Christianity. Third. It's almost always coupled with the desire to force those sacrifices and convictions on other people."

"I don't feel that."

Young Jolyon smiled: "That's because you're so solid."

In the pause that followed was heard the clucking, guggling noise of Anthony savouring his first glass of port.

Danaë spoke first: "Well, when you two have quite done talking all that twaddle, perhaps you'll tell me when you want me to come to Robin Hill?"

"Any time this month or next. Will you come too, Sol?"

Solomon hesitated, the colour deepening in his sturdy cheeks. He said, almost bashfully: "No, Jo; I shall be at the orchard."

Young Jolyon smiled, and dropped the subject. To Solomon's orchard there hung a tale.

Five years before, returning late one night from a theatre, Solomon was timidly accosted in the street by a quite young girl in a thin, shabby dress, with a face reddened by cold, a short upper lip, and large grey black-encircled eyes. She spoke with a Welsh accent, and seemed very tired.

Solomon, who was incapable of roughness, did not reject

her with the scorn and horror that he ought to have shown; he gave her a smile, gently shook his head, and stood looking at her. She looked so cold and unhappy, and her eyes so unhappy, that he began to talk to her. He ended by taking her to his rooms. A week later he bought a cottage in the country, with two acres of old orchard; here he took the girl and installed her. And here he had maintained her in sin ever since. She was the daughter of a small Welsh hill-farmer, new to her profession, into which she had been forced in the usual way. She had not indeed had time to get over its first horrors, and when Solomon had spoken gently to her while she sat holding her wet-stockinged feet to the fire in his sitting-room, she had suddenly and without affectation broken into a violent fit of sobbing. Her name was Anna Lewis, but Solomon called her Tansy.

The two acres of ground which surrounded the cottage were now scientifically laid out for fruit; a large crop of excellent apples, cherries, and pears was produced every year; for Solomon had given himself and most of the time he could spare from London, to this pursuit, in which his heart was concerned as it certainly was not in his Directorships. Young Jolyon, who had stayed with him there, alone knew the story; but since that which is secret must necessarily be naughty, 'Solomon's orchard' had become a by-word, and no one seriously believed that he grew fruit. The girl seldom showed herself beyond the precincts of that grove of trees; she wore her dark hair in a round knob on her pretty head, dressed in linen, worked in the orchard, made no pretences, sang and laughed all the time Solomon was with her, and went about dropping tears when he was not. She had a certain wild-raspberry refinement, and never jarred the nerves of Solomon, whose own mother had been Welsh. He had never thought of marrying her.

And so young Jolyon dropped the subject and said to Anthony: "Will you come too, sir? My father would be so delighted; he often says he never sees anything of you now."

Anthony inclined his head; his lips moved, his eyes gleamed friendlily.

Young Jolyon turned to Danaë: "Shall I ask Vigil?"

"Oh, yes! Ask Gregory; it'll do him good."

She was thinking: 'George doesn't like Gregory—poor Gregory.' A smile curling her upper lip revealed the gleam of her teeth.

"But why don't *you* like him?" she asked suddenly.

Young Jolyon was taken aback. "Like him? But I like him very much."

"Oh, no! You're afraid of him."

Young Jolyon bit his lip; habitually examining statements against himself, he did not at once reply.

"You're right," he said at last. "I'm afraid of him. I feel he might at any moment try to prevent my getting my own way." And catching again the infinitely quizzical look in Anthony's little eye, he felt ashamed of himself. "I don't mean that he would succeed, but he would try; he might put me to a lot of trouble to prevent his success."

Solomon said in his slow easy way: "I don't understand all that. Old Gregory's an excellent chap."

And, looking from his face to Danaë's, young Jolyon was conscious that he was talking Greek. Anthony alone had understood him. And young Jolyon, with the secret desire of delivering a counter-thrust, asked: "How are you getting on at the Bhang and Sciatic, sir?"

With a frown, Anthony answered: "Capitally."

Solomon said: "We're going to have a strike, Jo. What do you think about the Labour question?"

"I read two rather good things in the paper the other day. This was one: 'The loosening of the marriage tie and the decrease of the number of children per marriage is a certain sign of national decay.' That was by an Archdeacon.

The other was a Conservative politician: 'Publicly defrayed Labour schemes for persons out of employment will merely accelerate the deterioration of the nation.' They reminded me of a man at the seaside, dragging dead herring about in a cart, and crying: 'All alive o!' Those conceptions of marriage and economy have been out of the sea too long; no amount of 'All alive o!' will keep the breath in them. The State doesn't grow in any other direction and leave marriage and economy behind. The same with the Labour question; you must level it up with the conditions all round it!'"

Anthony, looking fixedly at him, replied: "I don't agree with you at all."

Young Jolyon smiled. "No, I don't suppose you do, sir. You believe in 'every man for himself'; you're an individualist. If you'll forgive my saying so, you're peculiarly national. But I think you capitalists forget that what's sauce for the goose is sauce for the gander. There's no real Socialistic feeling in this country; the workman's every bit as much of an individualist as you are."

"That's our strength."

"Pardon me—your weakness. Each workman looks to his own future; his individualism, hopefulness, selfishness, obstinacy, idealism, call it what you like—to his mainspring —and, banded together as they now are and will be more and more, they constitute a far more intense and fearful force than if they were animated by any of the brotherhood business. Each man of them means getting his own, their Unions are means to an end, not the end itself; that makes for strength."

"You think so?"

"Certainly. Even those men like Simon Harnutt (Vigil, by the way, is one of that sort) who seem to be most wrapped up in advancing the good of others, are really only impelled by the itch of getting their own beliefs and views adopted by others; they're individualists to a man, just like yourself."

"You seem to have studied the question."

"I have. We lookers-on see most of the game. And by Jove, sir, the more you hold them off at arm's length, the more you capitalists jut out at the other end of the social tree, with your Trusts and Combinations and 'don't care a damn' attitude, the more terrific is the struggle that's coming. I believe," young Jolyon ended gloomily, "the struggle in England—which will come more slowly than abroad, because it means more—there's more 'tusk' and character behind it—will bang Gallagher."

Anthony, fixing him with his little eye, said: "We shall see who will win."

With a contemptuous little curl of the lip young Jolyon remarked: "You prefer, in fact, sitting on the valve."

"I'm a good weight."

"And suppose, while you are sitting in deep thought on the valve, it occurs to you that you have made a mistake, will you go on sitting there?"

Anthony's little eyes twinkled: "Till the Day of Judgment."

"Which," replied young Jolyon, "will surely come."

For answer Anthony pushed the decanter towards his guest. Danaë rose. "You can sit and talk your politics," she said, "I'm going in to the drawing-room."

She went out. At the piano she sat humming a Spanish song. She was thinking of George.

Solomon returned to the Labour question.

"Do you know Sim Harnutt?" he said.

"Yes; my governor had a strike in the Rhyndy Pandy Coalfields last year, and Harnutt came down to us at Robin Hill."

"What's he like?"

"An idealist; an individualist. Very able."

"But to look at?"

"Flat-cheeked, close-jawed, wiry, clean-shaven, medium height, wears his hair rather long, looks like an American —and he's got that peculiar kind of haunting eye that always goes with his type."

"Is he a humbug?"

"Not at all. He doesn't mean what he says, but that's not his fault."

"How?"

"He talks about men being equal. It's the outward sign of the ideal he believes that he believes in; what he really believes in is Sim Harnutt, which is of course as much as to say that he doesn't believe in other men; in other words, that other men are not his equal. Besides, he has an obvious contempt for University creatures and capitalists like us."

Solomon beamed. "I should like to meet him," he said.

In an armchair Anthony sat slowly absorbing a large dark cigar through a rectangular meerschaum holder; now and then he slowly turned his little eyes on his son and guest, but he thought of nothing, sunk in after-dinner beatitude.

It was late when Solomon and young Jolyon took their departure, and past midnight when a man rang the bell of the flat, and stood waiting outside. His hands were thrust deep into the pockets of a dark overcoat with silk facings, which was open and revealed dress clothes; he held his high shoulders hunched, his chin thrust forward; his thin, long legs, the legs of a horseman, were a little bowed at the knees. Round his long, narrow head, under an opera hat, showed close-cropped reddish hair; he had a white, thin-lipped, freckled face, a clipped red moustache, and little fiery brown eyes.

The door was opened, and Danaë, in a mauve wrapper, a candle on her hand, asked:

"Who's that? What do you want? Jaspar? You've been drinking."

The visitor frowned; his eyes burned like coals.

"A little," he said in a clear voice. "Let me in!"

Danaë opened the door; and the two stood confronting one another. A smile played round Bellew's lips.

"You look very pretty with your hair like that. I've come to sleep."

"At this time of night indeed! There's no room for you!"

"I'll sleep in the passage."

Over Danaë's round, fresh face, framed in golden brown locks, over the curves of her ripe lips, into her greenish eyes, there came a smile—a half-coquettish, half-motherly, wholly hospitable smile.

"Well, come along!" she said: "there's my room after all!"

He closed the door behind him; the light from the candle fell on that strange smile. She gave a soft laugh, and finished with a sigh. She was thinking: "If Gregory could see me now!"*

1905–1906.

---

* From here "The Country House" opens, in its definitive form, and though George (Forsyte) Pendyce and Helen (Danaë) Bellew are important characters in that novel, Mrs. Pendyce is henceforward the central and most important character, not to speak of the Spaniel John.

WATER

I

THE incomparable ramifications of London City were immersed in fog, yellow and tortuous, corkscrewing through closed windows, and into the souls of men. Henry Cursitor, however, absorbed in the need of floating the new debentures of the "Rangoon Wayside Water Works Trust," had resisted its influence steadily all day. He was sustained perhaps by a Burmese sky roseate with the glow of his incurable optimism. Times were bad, but one would find the money. The British Empire—in a sense—depended on it, or if not precisely the British Empire, at least the position of Henry Cursitor. The two phenomena had become inextricably involved in a soul, not so much corrupted by a weak idealism, as accustomed to think in terms of an industrial development, without which its occupation would be gone. Fellows with their noses slightly on one side, and blue eyes upturned and shining, were anathema to Henry Cursitor—their optimism had no sense of the immediate, which experience had told him was the only real obstacle to progress, including his own. If he had an enemy, it was the tightness of money. Considering that money must know by now that it would ultimately be found it was absurdly, heart-breakingly close and evasive. It seemed to enjoy playing with the hearts, nay the lives, of those whose only wish was to water the soil of business, promote the steady flow of industry. Since, a quarter of a century ago, his father's permanganate of potash Works had offered Henry Cursitor, briefless barrister, a seat on the Board, he had clung to Direction, going down on ship after ship, simply owing to the tightness of money. It seemed to have a grudge against him for having so often got the better of it, for having raised it here and there, seen it earn stirring dividends, then slowly slip into the deep, raised it again, and set out on a fresh ship.

"The Rangoon Wayside Water Works Trust" was not an altogether fresh ship; it had indeed been slowly sinking ever since the war; but it merely needed this fresh issue of debentures to plug its sides and fit it once more for the empyrean. In these cases the difficulty was always, of course, to frame the prospectus, so as to find the money without concealing the truth that, without money, the "Rangoon W.W.W.T." would nose-dive, and carry Henry Cursitor down with it, this time possibly for good.

Before a sheet of foolscap, his hair smooth and dark, his thin nose jutting, his eyes peaty and reflective (his mother had been a Ferguson), his clean-shaven lips and cheeks ruddy in the yellow light, he sat still, and rather bitter.

One got little credit for doing one's job, and keeping the flag flying. When he thought of the numbers of men who had ratted from the ships that had gone down with him, without ever raising a finger to raise money, he felt as if there were something sacred in his own career. Never any lack of fair-weather fellows, of guinea-pigs, who, when it came to weathering the storm, left it all to him!

With a slow pen he traced the words: "These public utility Works, soundly conceived, now need only the final touch of this small issue to place them firmly on a dividend-bearing basis. Carrying seven per cent, and secured on the whole property of the Trust, these preferred debentures constitute an exceptional investment. The directors confidently appeal"——he wished the deuce they did! They had not succeeded in getting it underwritten——a sinister sign! For a moment he envisaged the failure of that appeal—— saw "The Rangoon W.W.W.T." under a pitiless blue sky, and the pitiless tropical rain, a mass of scrap-iron, jumbled concrete and wood; and, with the gesture of a man who dismisses a bad dream, added the words: "to the Public," and blew his nose.

"Watnot," he said to the Secretary, "we must get it out this week. There are two big issues due next Monday."

"Yes, sir, I'll have it with the printers to-night. Do you think we shall get the money?"

"We must, Watnot."

"Yes, sir."

He was sorry for little Watnot and his five hundred a year—a married man, three children. Still, they would get the money, must get it, for though not married himself, he, too, had to live. And he began re-reading the prospectus, to see whether he could truthfully strengthen it. When he had finished it was clear to him that he could not; indeed, one or two paragraphs challenged the future in somewhat striking fashion. But the Public were so lethargic that it was always necessary to bring possibilities vividly before them. The market was milked with difficulty in days like these. He thought, with a certain discouragement, of that thin blue trickle, and those personal efforts on the 'phone and in the offices of bankers and other moneyed persons, which he had so often found necessary, to thicken it. Handing the sheets to Watnot he filled his pipe and leaned back, dreaming for a moment of that retirement which always appeared to him desirable when he had to raise money. What a relief to give up Directorship, and devote himself to wood-carving, and breeding rabbits; to pass the burden on to others, and see them stagger under it and go down. That was the trouble! In his experience, if you didn't do the job yourself, nobody did it; and that was why he was always baulked of his intermittent longings to have done with it all. It was a matter of secret self-esteem. If one couldn't believe that one was a better Direc-

tor than other men—one would feel that one had wasted
one's life. And, since one *was* a better Director, there was
nothing for it but to carry on! If only carrying-on didn't
mean raising money! He sighed, and blew a cloud of
smoke. To raise money, not for oneself, but for industry
—nothing ignoble about that, only—tiring! Yes, and
sometimes impossible. But this time it must not be impossible—"The Rangoon W.W.W.T." was the last plank
between him and bankruptcy. Never! Sooner than that—
well, something would turn up! Going to the window, he
stared into the fog. Behind him little Watnot was getting
into his coat and hat, to go to the printer with the draft
prospectus. Cursitor heard him close the door. London!
All the result of money that had been raised! He felt be-
wildered. Where on earth did it all come from? His mind
groped for a moment with the child-like wonder of a man
who had been raising money for so long that he had lost
all sense of its origin. Money made money, of course!
That is, it paid those who dug and ploughed and fished,
and bred animals and trees, and burrowed for minerals,
and—er—the rest of it! And after payment of those far-
away people there was money over, from manipulation of
what they extracted from the soil; that would be, of course,
the money that he raised—to make money with, or—not.

A knock on the door took him back to his chair, and he
said:

"Come in."

A man entered. "Mr. Henry Cursitor?"

"Yes."

"My name is Gerard Deacon. I was referred to you by
Mr. Markham Mays."

"Oh! Will you sit down?"

While his visitor took the edge of a chair, Cursitor
coldly studied his appearance. He seemed to be about forty,
and had on a blue suit, of a shade which suggested the

Colonies, over a shirt of a deeper blue, with its own collar, which still more suggested the Colonies. A red silk tie set off a face uniformly yellow, with steel-grey eyes burnt in the rims, and a short grizzly-brown moustache over a sensitive mouth, complemented by a firm but bearded jaw.

"Yes?" said Cursitor.

"I understand from Mr. Mays, sir, that you might be open to consider the floating of a company, or at all events the raising of money to work a scheme in Australia."

"I am afraid," said Cursitor, "my hands are full. Why didn't you take it to Markham Mays himself?"

A faint smile appeared on the face, which was already giving Cursitor something of a turn, as if its owner were alone in the room.

"I did; but his hands were full." The voice was educated, but had a toneless slightly nasal quality, as if unaccustomed to speech. "It seems that money's very difficult to raise."

"It is," said Cursitor.

"I'm sorry. It's something quite exceptional."

With a little smile Cursitor was thinking: Never knew it not to be—when he was struck by his visitor's rising and walking to the door. He had never seen such a thing before, and said almost hastily:

"What is it—if I may ask?"

"Water."

"Yes," said Cursitor, "with water Australia would be another country."

He was surprised by the effect of these words. His visitor walked back to the table, and, staring straight before him, said:

"You people don't know what water is. You turn a tap and the blessed thing flows. I've nearly died of thirst a dozen times in a country that will grow anything, sir—any mortal thing, and grows nothing, just for want of what I

could give it to-morrow, if I could get the money. I know
a valley in the desert there that in ten years will make an
earthly paradise; when I say valley I mean a sort of im-
mensely wide depression in the desert level. And the water's
there; just wants the money, to tap an underground river."

"Underground river?"

"Just that."

Cursitor stared at his visitor, who had regained that
appearance of being alone in the room. Was the chap a
visionary, with those burnt-rimmed eyes of his? If there
was a being he couldn't stand, it was a visionary.

"That would be a long business," he said, "even if
you're right. But you'll excuse my asking how you discovered such a thing?"

His visitor smiled.

"Simpler than falling off a log," he said. "Just where
that depression I speak of flattens out into the main desert,
I struck a rift in the sand one day. After about fifteen feet
the sand became rock, and the rift went down. I've got
an instinct for water; it's saved my life more than once. I
knew as sure as I'm in this room——" ('Is he?' thought
Cursitor, oddly) "that there was water down there. Well,
sir, I went back to my camp, and brought up a marked line
with a bit of iron on it, and let it down. The line went
slack in my hand at 270 feet; I'd bottomed the rift. I
pulled it up; the iron was wet, and the line, for nearly
twelve feet. There was a well down there, or an underground lake, or a river—which? I took off the iron and
put on it a bit of wood instead and let it down again. At
260 feet it ran through my fingers like greased lightning.
That meant a river! I let 50 feet go, and pulled it up.
There were 60 feet of wet line when I got it to ground—
ten feet of depth and fifty of current, you see. I tried it
again, a dozen times; always the same result. Then I tried
the line slipping through my fingers; in ten seconds 170

feet ran through. Seventeen feet a second is just over twelve miles an hour. An underground river ten to twelve feet deep of that force. Width I couldn't gauge, of course, but with that depth it should be considerable. Just think of that force of water running to waste down there, beneath a soil that you need only sprinkle to grow anything. That's my secret, sir, and I've come home to sell it, or rather I've come home to tap that river and make a Garden of Eden of a desert where there's nothing but sand and brush."

With these words his visitor went back, as it were, to his desert. So still and remote was he that Cursitor had no difficulty in making several reflections. The fellow might be cracked, or again he might not, for he certainly had the look of the bush—the peculiar, half-vacant intensity of great dangerous spaces, and supreme loneliness. Cursitor remembered a cousin of his own, many years in Western Australia—the drained, strained look of his face. One had to be so careful! This thought—first indication that he was considering the proposition—surprised him. Garden of Eden! Your grandfather! And yet—— Wonderful things were done with water—something inspiring, romantic in those great conversions! At bottom all industry was founded on them. A pulse began beating in his forehead, not precisely blood to the head, but a warning of the hope which sprang perennial in his nature. No! One couldn't be too careful.

"Deacon, you said, I think?"

"Gerard Deacon."

"Can you refer me to——"

His visitor smiled. "Kangaroos—black fellahs—I've been out there since I was twenty. I could give you a reference to a store keeper in Baragawoollah!"

"Your family, perhaps?" said Cursitor.

"My father was an Oxford don—he's dead. I've got

a brother in the Church, I believe; but in a place where you get mail but once a year, one loses touch. You might find him in a directory, I suppose, but he hasn't seen me since I was twenty."

"I see," said Cursitor. "To raise money in these days, sir, requires very definite inducements to put before people. One needs to be certain of the possibilities. The opinion of an expert in hydraulics would be wanted, and then there's the whole question of whether the plan's feasible in the large." His visitor continued to stare at kangaroos or whatever he was seeing in the fog outside.

"I see," he said again. "Well, I suppose I'll have to go to the Government." And he turned towards the door.

"The Government!" said Cursitor, in sheer surprise. "Good Lord! They'll ask for two hydraulic reports, and the opinions of half a dozen experts before they'll let you upstairs."

His visitor turned once more.

"Why? They want to develop Australia; isn't it vital to them?"

"Certainly. But they won't spend a penny on verification. Unless you get evidence in black and white, you needn't go *there*."

"Oh! I've only been back a week, but I thought by the look of the people here, you'd be glad to be shut of some of them."

"No doubt; but the Government in this country has to have things done for it. That's where we come in."

"But you don't come in. So long!"

"One moment," said Cursitor almost hurriedly. "Where are you staying?"

"Golden Gate Hotel, Covent Garden. Name struck me—in this climate of yours."

"I should like to think the matter over. I'll see Markham Mays, and write to you."

With his hand on the door the visitor remained silent a moment; then he said fiercely:

"That desert nearly did me in three times; I've sworn to get even with it."

Cursitor, who had dropped his eyes to avoid the sight of a fierceness so unbusiness-like, raised them again. His visitor was gone.

He sat, with a slight smile curling his lips beneath his somewhat jutting nose, staring at great yellow spaces under a brilliant sun. The fog, in fact, was very yellow in the street, and they had just lighted the lamps. In all his experience he had never had so wild-cat a proposition made to him, nor one that so titillated some unacknowledged instinct. Like all who have to do with companies, he prided himself on a practicality which took nothing at its face value. This was why he seemed to see that great yellow space turn green. He was still staring at it when little Watnot returned.

"It's in the printer's hands, sir; we shall get it out on Thursday."

"Oh! Ah!" said Cursitor; he said it with a certain lightness, as though the "Rangoon W.W.W.T." was not after all the sole plank between him and bankruptcy.

"Very foggy, Watnot! We want—er—water."

Little Watnot stared. "Rain, sir?" he said.

II

LIKE all true promoters of industry, Cursitor accepted the inevitable. Whether, as an Arctic animal grows its fur, he had grown the quality in connection with his environment, or whether it is one without which people do not promote industry—is doubtful. In any case, it was as well. Money was tight; the debenture issue a frost so black that 'The

Rangoon W.W.W.T.' began settling down at once; six months would see her bones lying on the ocean bed and fishes scuttling between her ribs. And yet, while contemplating this submarine landscape, Cursitor would suddenly see land so dry that it wanted water. Coming from the stock-brokers in charge of the issue, with the news: "No, sir, it doesn't move," he walked almost insensibly into the office of Markham Mays. That well-known chairman of the Brisbane and Perth Concessions Limited had just completed his morning's work. Having signed his name four hundred times, he had his hat in his hand. On seeing Cursitor he assumed it.

"Ah! Cursitor, I'm just going out to lunch."

Looking at that well-clothed face with small but Napoleonic features, and hearing the comfortable drawl, Cursitor felt a kind of envy. Markham Mays was so successful. Able, of course, but some fellows had all the luck.

"I shan't keep you a minute," he said; "it's about a fellow you sent to me."

"Oh!" said Markham Mays: "Come and have lunch. I always lunch west; it doesn't take so long."

Cursitor, one of those who snatch a cup of coffee standing, or bite a sandwich while their pen traces the words: 'I have perused your report on the alkali deposits in Cochin China'—said that he couldn't spare the time; and was soon rolling west in Markham Mays' car.

In the handsome old-fashioned setting of Burton's Club, Markham Mays looked more natural.

"Turkish coffee?" he said at last. "What did you want me to do?"

"A man called Gerard Deacon you sent to me about an Australian water proposition."

Markham Mays emitted a slow, able laugh.

"Oh! that chap? Mad as a March hare."

"Then why did you send him to me?" asked Cursitor.

"Couldn't think of anyone else at the moment."

"You wanted him out of the room?"

"I did; but he'd have gone without. No, I was sorry for the poor beggar; he's got water on the brain. Dozens of those chaps in Australia—bush crazy."

Cursitor frowned. "What brought him to you?"

Like a rich blessing the laugh emerged again. "He said he was attracted by the words: 'Brisbane to Perth' in the director's *Who's Who*."

In Cursitor hostility had begun fermenting. "So you pushed him off on me!"

"I wanted to give the poor devil a chance. Odd coincidence—his father was my tutor at Oxford, old Jeremy Deacon—awful good sort, but dreamy as they make 'em."

That at least was some corroboration of Deacon's story. Not so fast! Markham Mays was not infallible. He felt a wave of sympathy with that yellow lonely man in the blue shirt.

"Well," he said, "I'm not so sure the chap's cracked."

The long quizzical regard which followed, annoyed him greatly. Markham Mays might be able, but he was almost offensive.

"I must be getting back," he said abruptly. "Thanks!" and took his leave. So much for Deacon and his water proposition—he would think of it no more, wasting his time!

The Golden Gate Hotel in Covent Garden was a flat yellowish edifice with a past-mastery of cheerlessness, carried through to its very entrails. Enquiry of a sort of 'boots' was followed by a long pause. Cursitor remained standing in a little cheerless lounge with red-baize curtains, three spittoons, two small tables with stained marble tops, and a picture of the Coronation of Queen Victoria, above a cast-iron grate. He had just decided to wait no longer when the sort of 'boots' poked his head in, said: "Gent comin' down," and poked his head out again. At that moment the commonsense in Cursitor, developed by raising money during a quarter of a century, bade him 'cut his lucky'; only belief in his own judgment and self-control, and some obscure instinct, kept him standing there with his back to the door, between the spittoon at his feet and the Coronation at his head. A voice said:

"Ah! It's you."

Its nasal refinement was reassuring; after all, Deacon was a gentleman. He turned and held out his hand.

"I've just come from Markham Mays. Perhaps you've been able to do something with your proposition?"

A faint smile answered him. "You've got too much water in this country."

Cursitor nodded. "Yes," he said; "but I've been in Arizona. They've done wonderful things with water there."

"I've taken my passage back. Why not come and see for yourself?"

Cursitor laughed. "Australia? Fantastic! I'm afraid I'm much too busy."

Was he? Was he not rather just the opposite, with the 'R.W.W.W.T.' hopelessly on the rocks? Was not this, in fact, the moment for a Napoleonic stroke, to push back the closing doors of Fate? And he stood contemplating the blue shirt and the yellow face above it, bluer and yellower than ever in the stronger light of a clear day.

"How long would it take?" he said suddenly.

"By land to Sicily you could be back in five months. The sand storms should be over before you get there. Look here!" He drew an old map from his breast pocket, and spread it on the coffee-stained marble. Cursitor noticed little stains, too, as of coffee about his lips and beard, and was conscious of a sickly odour as they bent side by side above the map.

"Here," said Deacon, "is Baragawoollah—my place is

two days on, and it's five days south from there. Hundred and fifty miles from the coast—about here;" he placed his finger on a spot where Cursitor could see no names; "all desert—not a station, not a tree—not a well—nothing. Pure sand, and a little stunted bush."

"And that goes on?"

"Four hundreds of miles; right into the centre."

"What a country!"

"Yes," the voice sounded far away; "it's a corker."

Cursitor looked up. His companion was so obviously alone with the 'corker' that he hardly liked putting the question:

"Have you gone into the cost at all?"

"No," said the thin flat voice with its slightly nasal twang; "I'm not an engineer."

"H'm!" said Cursitor. The proposition was too 'wild-cat' altogether; not the slightest use to think of it. The fellow was speaking:

"I see that damned country green as the grass on the earth, flowing with milk and honey; grapes from thorns, figs from thistles. Talk of conversion, what's the conversion of the human soul compared with the conversion of the soil? The soul does its little stunt and passes, the soil remains and breeds the bodies without which there are no souls."

Cursitor put on his hat. What a way to express the need for developing industry!

"Good-bye!" he said.

"So long! My boat leaves on the 30th. The *Olla Podrida;* you could join her at Suez."

Cursitor went out, murmuring to himself, "Not likely!"

In the Tube on the way back to the City he began to calculate. The General Meeting of the "Rangoon W.W. W.T." was not for seven months; nothing much would happen before then. 'If money gets looser,' he thought—

'but money'll be tight or loose whether I'm here or not.' Of course he would be here.

While crossing from the Bank station to his office he suffered from a sort of nausea—so many people, all raising money in competition with each other! Oh! for the sun, and a touch of Nature! The sun was absent but the touch of Nature was not far off.

Little Watnot had a cold.

"The issue doesn't bove, sir; it doesn't bove," he said.

"I know that," said Cursitor irritably. "There's no money in this country. I'm not going to sit here and wait for the ship to go down, Watnot. I've a good mind to try and raise it in Australia. They've more sense of water, there."

Little Watnot sneezed; what a rabbit the fellow was! Cursitor did not stay long. He did not stay long anywhere in the days that followed—uncontrollably restless. Whether in his bachelor flat at Westminster, in his office, or on his golf-course, he wished to be somewhere else. He longed for the society of people with a wide view of things, or for the society of no one but himself. He bought books on water, and surprised acquaintances by asking them such questions as: "Suppose you have a current running twelve miles an hour, and drop a nine-inch pipe into it, how many feet will your water be forced up, without artificial aid?"

And when they answered: "About two," he looked at them with a certain distaste. His compatriots seemed to him lamentably sunk in the immediate struggle for an unpleasant existence. The British Empire had never before loomed so large in his consciousness—and all founded on water! Not that he was thinking for a minute of that lonely yellow chap and his 'wild-cat' proposition. No, he was thinking of the "Rangoon W.W.W.T." with a growing certainty that there was money to be raised for it in Melbourne, Sydney, Brisbane, Adelaide and Perth. No good sitting down and waiting for the end! . . .

He joined the S.S. *Olla Podrida* at Suez. He scanned the list of passengers, anxious not to be reminded of that visionary fellow. He found the name among the second-cabin passengers. With a little care, then, he would see nothing of him, for, as befitted one whose business was to raise money, himself was in the saloon, and his name not in the list issued at Marseilles. He felt light-hearted in that brilliant sunshine, with so much water about, and kept his letters of introduction in his breast pocket—more and more convinced that there would be money to be had for the asking. He went on shore at Colombo, strolled in the Cinnamon Gardens, and watched a mango-tree grown while he waited. That same night, too hot to sleep, and slightly drunk on the scent from the spicy shore, he was leaning over the rail forward when a voice said: "Your first sight of the Southern Cross?" Yellower than ever, and at least as lonely-looking, in his eternal blue shirt, that chap was leaning there beside him. It was like the end or the beginning of a dream, and Cursitor bit hard on his pipe.

"The place to see it from's the bush—it's company there. So you're coming up with me to have a look at the water, after all."

"No fear," said Cursitor abruptly.

"Pleasure trip, then?" said the refined and nasal voice.

"No. I've come in connection with a concern I direct in Rangoon."

"I see. This is an Australian boat."

"I know that," said Cursitor pettishly. "I'm going to Melbourne." And for a moment he thought wildly of rushing up on to the Bridge and demanding to be put back on shore. The ship blew suddenly her melancholy whistle.

"Moving," said the voice. "I shall just catch the coast-ing steamer at Perth. I've a notion that I can trace out where that river comes near the surface. The ground drops gradually away—in three or four miles the bush should be at least two hundred feet lower."

"Ah!" said Cursitor distantly. There was silence, and under the blazing stars he watched the land slowly fade, the tropic trees blurring into dark loom, the lights shifting into scarcity. But still the breath of the land reached him —heavy-sweet.

"No stink about the bush," said the voice, "clean air. You ought to have a look at Australian desert: it's not a common product. I'll 'larn it to be a toad,' yet."

Turning to see the expression that accompanied those slow, vengeful words, Cursitor was once more conscious of the faint peculiar odour he had noticed once before. The fellow smelled like some plant or other. Was it the result of living in the bush?

During the next ten days Cursitor lived constantly a double life. Whenever he saw that visionary fellow he was possessed by an irritable commonsense; but at other moments, especially under the starry sky of night, he was ridden by a sort of longing. Fortune, the British Empire, Henry Cursitor & Co.! Would there be any harm in just seeing for himself? It committed him to nothing; would not take him more than six weeks or so, the fellow said. Ought one to throw away any chance? Suppose that river could be tapped near the surface—what enormous possibilities! No difficulty in raising money to develop them. Arizona had done it—the fertile square miles of alfalfa, cotton, tobacco, fruit, wheat, bordered with low banks and the cottonwood trees, golden under the February sun! All done by water! The sandy cactus desert, sweet-smelling of creosote bush, all around where water was not yet, within the filmy receding ring of violet mountains! a Garden of Eden growing like the mango-tree—while you waited. To be the man who worked another miracle like that, who watered the earth and industry till it teemed with men, and paid high dividends! Cursitor-land—to leave his name written on the map! Really it—— His eyes fell on that visionary chap gazing over the taffrail at the watery expanse—it was madness! . . .

He got off at Perth.

On the coasting steamer he was almost unapproachable. It was so small that he and that fellow took up most of it. They shared the only cabin; but Cursitor slept on the long seat in the saloon; he could not stand the fellow at such close quarters. They coasted for days under a brassy sun, while Cursitor poured cold water on himself and watched that chap—lonely, smiling to himself, imperturbable with his visions and his blue shirt. And the long Australian coast dragged by—sandy foothills and sandy foothills; with now and again a group of gum trees and roofs of corrugated iron, and run-up shacks, and dreary boats coming off, with dreary bales and men; stores landed, and landed. And then for two days nothing but the long Australian coastline dragging by, too far away to show its worth. The mental discomfort of those days, the bitter sense of folly; the vision of the "Rangoon W.W.W.T." settling down and down, and he cut off by weeks and weeks from the power of raising money, from little Watnot and the cosy office, and money—money—all around. What a flat he had been!

'Baragawoollah!' There it was—corrugated iron and gum trees—a little lonely hump, dusky in the white coast haze, like a flea-bite on the side of a pointer dog. And Henry Cursitor, about to disembark there, with a kit bag and a visionary. Baragawoollah—Civilisation! Two days beyond, and five days beyond that! 'The chump I am!' he thought.

They went ashore in a lighter. All the next day, and the next, they drove together through the summer heat in a wagon behind mules. The wheels drove deep through rutted sand. There was no shade.

Deacon pointed out the features. Cursitor could not see them; and hardly ten minutes passed without his thinking: 'I was cracked.' They slept at stations. In their owners Cursitor noted the same 'rangey' stare of intent vacancy that Deacon had. Their boisterous welcomes suffered from eclipse; they were back at once, looking for something in the distance. 'That'll be water,' he thought. He noted the wells and little irrigation works, with a feeling of despair. It seemed to him like trying to wash a blanket by sneezing on it in a corner. On the second day a scant herbage had appeared, and there were sheep. At every meal, night and morning, Cursitor ate mutton and tomatoes and rank tea with preserved milk. He wondered how long it would be before his shirt turned blue and he acquired 'the stare.'

On the second evening as dusk fell, they arrived at Deacon's 'place.' Four black fellows and a Scotchman received them with an interest which centred almost at once on the contents of the wagon. Five thick gum trees sheltered the house. It was almost cool; and, entering the living-room, Cursitor experienced the first sense of comfort since leaving Perth. It contained long wicker chairs and books; a yellow dog got up and licked his hand—an Irish terrier with all its tail. A native woman brought in a yellow drink; it tasted of whisky, limes, and sugar.

"Home," said Deacon. "Do exactly as you like. This is a good chair. Grub'll be ready in an hour."

Alone in the long chair with the dog beside him, Cursitor looked out at the stars between the foliage of the gum trees, and a curious peace slid into his soul. This, then, was the edge! Beyond—Deacon had said—was 'nothing'; limitless unwatered waste; sand and the stars. And he had lived here twenty years! An odd reverence, like one of

those tricks of atmosphere in old Italian landscape paintings, coloured at that moment his vision of 'this fellow.'
What store within him of pluck and self-sufficiency! Or
was there breath of magic in this dry starry peace, and the
chap spell-bound—pickled in space and sand? And how
long would it take to pickle Henry Cursitor, so that he too
shook off the fret of raising money, and sat down upon
the edge of nothing? Absurd! The moon must be up behind the house, for all the gum-tree leaves were silver,
scimitar-shaped like the swords of Saracens, with a glitter
moving in a little wind. They had cut the stars out of
the sky; shredded them to powder, so that heaven was
chalky-blue, and earth below it dusted with chopped star.
And on that powdery surface the shadows of the gum
trees trickled out like deep blue water. 'I'll larn it to be a
toad.' The vengeful words did not tally with this pickled
peace. No, this chap had still the urge which twenty years
ago had sent him forth to land him on the edge of nothing; this urge to get further, and rive blood from stones,
water from sand. The sublime urge that had made a man's
world out of dry desert; brought industry to being, raised
money like water. To his ears came the thin, sweet wail-
ing of a black fella blowing on a shell, the gum-tree leaves
shook out a crisp and chancy rustle; the yowl of a dingo
wandered eerily, far out. And the Irish terrier licked Cursitor's hand with a dry tongue, exploring up his wrist for
moisture. It was homely; one thought of little Watnot.
In a day or two that chap in the blue shirt would take him
out to water in the dusty distance; till then—a sleep, a
dream.

III

THE last sheep seen on Deacon's place was a memory three
days old; no herbage now; and the only shade, their mov-

ing shadows. They marched from shadow-fall right on
through the night; and when their shadows began drying-
up under the climbing sun, lay down beneath a strip of
thin canvas painted with layers of red and yellow, inclined
on two thin steel stakes driven sloping into the sand. As
the sun shifted, their black fella rose from the lee of a
mule and shifted a stake so that they always had the ray-
disperser between them and the awful author of it all.
Stifling under it, they slept a little, ate a little, sucked limes
slowly, drank their allowances sip by sip, while their horses,
the black fella and the pack mules, eased of all gear,
drowsed in the grilling sun. One day more and black fella,
pack mules, water-skins and all would be left, and they
two, with a water skin apiece, would make a dash for it.
Cursitor suffered the tortures of a townsman no longer in
his youth, but was curiously uplifted. The night air was
cool, and the thought of nearing water stimulating as the
words of any prospectus he had ever issued. Listening to
the faint shuffle of their march through the bush silence,
watching their grotesque shadows moving over the moonlit
sand, he would compose invitations to the Public. "This
desirable countryside, with its perfect climate, and incalcu-
lably fertile—er—sand, needs only water to rival Mesopotamia in the days of the Chaldeans . . . Here we have
within—er—some thirty days of London a possible settling
ground of our surplus population, a new province which
may rival in productivity any tract of its size in the British
Empire. Tomatoes alone. . . . The appeal is made rather
from patriotic than from commercial . . ." No, that savoured of sentiment; keep to the pocket—even in time of
war those holders had demanded dividends. Investment
was investment. "A careful survey," his mind went on,
"has shown conclusively that, properly worked, there is no
limit to the possibilities. A light railway to the admirable
natural harbour of Baragawoollah"—his horse pecked sud-

denly, and Cursitor was thrown forward on his neck; the animal had not done this before—had he been listening? Recovering the upright, and a little shaken, Cursitor fixed his eyes on the Southern Cross. Wonderful, how Deacon stared out into this waste bereft of landmark—no trail, no tree, no hill! Did his nostrils scent that far-off water? He had hardly opened his mouth since they started, and Cursitor remembered his garrulous guide in Arizona saying: "In the desert when I'm workin' on the trail I've got no use for talk; no, sir." Odd, that in silence Cursitor's confidence should increase, for in all his experience so far, confidence in industry had depended on a flow of words.

The fourth morning revealed greyer sand and a sparse brush. They camped at a spot where there was a little brackish water, from which branched the tracks of dingoes.

"We shall jump off from here," said Deacon, when they camped. "Have a good sleep; you'll need it. We'll take these stakes along, but I left the lines up there. A night's ride, a day on the job, and a night's ride back. We can only just carry water enough. Due South by East, thirty-one miles."

Cursitor slept little; flies and ants and even butterflies affected this patch of brush; and he was scared. To dash into desert space with just enough water for survival! Suppose he got separated from Deacon; or this black fella decamped with the gear, while they were away, or the dingoes who came here to drink were to eat the mules, or there was one of those terrible sand-storms that Deacon had spoken of with awe! Suppose—suppose a hundred things! Dear memories of his lodgings, where nothing was ever disturbed from year's end to year's end; of the financial columns of *The Times;* of little Watnot, and other fixed objects, mingled with his fears, the burning sun, and the bites of ants, to keep him wakeful.

Whenever he opened his eyes Deacon was seated cross-

legged, gazing at distance, like a Mussulman with his mind
on Mecca. In a quarter of a century of raising money for
industry in the British Empire, he had never known such
hours of exquisite discomfort. And they were but preamble
of the still more exquisite! He was tempted in direct
crescendo to say to Deacon: 'I'm sorry, but I feel bad, I
must wait for you here.' If only he had brought a clinical
thermometer, raised in hot water to 106 before they started. But alas! he had not a sign of fever with him. He
had even got over his stiffness, and though bitten and un-
shorn, was conscious of a certain rude health. No! If he
refused, it must be on the grounds of the insecurity of this
business. He must say quite calmly: 'Now that I've seen
the nature of the country I feel it's useless to go further;
you could never get the money to exploit such God-forsaken
desert. It would need the faith of Early Christians.
There's nothing Early Christian about investors.' As a
fact, he was not so sure—he had known cases of belief in
the miraculous, when it was properly put to them. Still, a
desert like this could not be properly put—a country drier
than Arizona! Twice he sat up, moistening his parched
lips for the effort, but sight of that motionless fellow, burnt
to the deepest yellow above his blue shirt, the feeling that
his words—like the buzzing of the flies—would be lost on
that fixed visionary, overpowered him, and he sank down
again to wait for a better moment. But he would do it—
he was resolved, he would *not* go further with this insane
adventure . . .

At six o'clock they started. They went at the usual foot
pace, with a large water-skin securely fastened behind each
of their saddles. As the sun heeled over, the pace drew
out into the loping shuffle of the bush. The day went down
in beauty of opal and violet; for a few minutes the bush
trembled with radiance, then the darkness rushed together,
and they were riding by starlight. With the first fresh-

ness Cursitor's curious optimism came back with an almost
lyrical note . . . "Only those who have seen the beauty of
the bush at sunset, drunk in the nectar of the pure night
air, can conceive the——er——this wonderful paysage . . ."
Wrong; no foreign words to the British Public! "has a
quality all its own. Disease is unknown there." No need
to add "and so are people" . . . that was implicit to those
who read between the lines, and as for those who didn't,
well——the raising of money rather depended on that. He
touched his horse with his heel. In three hours they left
all trace of brush again, and were on pure sand. Cursitor
hoped that they were leaving heavy hoof-marks. Away
from the pack mules, their dark shapes, the jingle of their
little bells, the weird mule-cries of the black fella, this
ride out into immensity produced sensations at once proud
and timorous. He had stuck it, was seeing it through! He
could fancy little Watnot's eyes rounder and rounder at
his tale of the darkness, the loneliness. He must remember to tell him how the stars glittered, of the ghostly colour
of the sand, and the dead silence! That chap in front of
him, steering on, with the great water-skin behind, was a
shape grotesque, as of some primeval jar reared on two
moving legs! Deacon and he loping through the starry dark
——spirits of water riding to the aid of their own element——
through hostile wastes! His horse pecked. The water-skin
behind him wobbled against his back. It sent his mood veer-
ing to the timorous. If only Deacon would speak now and
then, and break this awful silence——this sense of being dis-
embodied and at large, in wilderness, clean out of touch
with all reality. Or, was this reality, and all that he had
known so far, unreal? This was the most terrifying
thought he had yet had. To be alone with the primal source
of money, with the earth before it had been operated on;
alone and nomad as the black fellas, nay, rather as the very
dingoes! His mind wandered painfully. From this desert

unscratched by man, to the City of London—what a long
way! Water! Mesopotamia—of old a desert between two
rivers; watered and scratched, and on it the mightiest,
most teeming cities of the past; desert once more, unwatered and unscratched! Water! No wonder mirage
took the form of water, water everywhere, nor any drop
to drink! A tricky thing—water; his safest experience
with it had been in connection with capital. He remembered two or three occasions when he had watered capital,
with distinct advantage.

The two-legged jar in front of him ceased moving suddenly; Deacon had reined up.

"Ten minutes," he said; "better stretch your legs. Don't
let go of your horse! Here comes the moon."

Cursitor looked back. The moon, in round, like a bright,
cunning face, was peering at him from the edge of a swelling on the plain. 'I'll whiten your bones,' it seemed to say.
God! What a beastly thought! He took a long breath.

"I suppose," he said, "you know your way. But how on
earth you do, I can't think."

Deacon laughed. "Due South by East—the stars!"

'Stars!' thought Cursitor. 'He's only got one—fixed—
this blessed water. I only hope it won't go in.'

"Ready?" said Deacon: "On we go."

His shape, no longer like a jar borne up on moving legs
—tittuped ahead in level moonlight, and Cursitor, following, saw his own shadow slink out in front of him on the
grey sand, it was as if his spirit were leading his body on.
To—what—to water? . . .

IV

"WE ought to be thereabouts; I must wait for the sun.
Give me your horse."

Dreadfully tired, Cursitor resigned the rein and lay

down on the sand; it felt soft as a bed, softer than he had
known it yet. In two minutes he was asleep. He had a perfect dream——Fenchurch Street with a stream of water
flowing down its middle. . . . When he woke the sun was
up. The two horses were tethered to one of the steel stakes
driven deep in between two humps of saddle heaped with
sand. An empty water-skin lay squash on the ground——the
horses had evidently been watered. The other, still full
and swelling, lay out of reach of the tether ropes. Cursitor,
parched and miserably sore, stood up. No sign of Deacon,
save footmarks leading to the West, judged by the sun,
risen perhaps two hours. Cursitor noticed that the sand was
different in look from any he had seen——loose, more yellow,
thick and soft, almost like seashore sand——the feet had
sunk deep in. He stood still and tried to utter a 'Cooee!'
It was always a difficult sound for him, and his throat
was parched; and going to the water-skin, he cautiously
undid the mouthpiece. Even that tepid water revived him,
and he began to feel hungry. After eating some meat and
a biscuit, he lit his pipe. Deacon was evidently prospecting;
they must have hit the spot very nearly or he would not
have tethered the horses and gone on foot.

The surface of the plain swelled and dipped just here——
a man's walking figure might be lost to sight within a mile;
but, making such tracks, he could not lose himself. And
to that lonely townsman in this waste, the thought was reassuring. When Deacon had located the rift, he would
come back on his track and fetch him. For two hours he
waited in slow increasing torture of heat and loneliness.
Couldn't the fellow find the place? Had he sprained his
ankle, or had sunstroke? In the third hour of that grilling
heat a thought brought him to his knees, scooping at the
sand. He had scooped to the depth of nearly two feet before he found resistance. Good God! All this surface
sand was new, was a sand-drift. There must have been one

of those ghastly sand-storms which sometimes obliterated everything——so Deacon said——for miles, till another great wind came and swept it further on. But if Deacon couldn't find the rift, why didn't he come back? Two searchers were better than one. He looked at the horses. Dared he leave them, and go off on Deacon's tracks? Would he feel safer with the horses and the water-skin, or following those human footmarks? Suppose, while he was finding Deacon the horses got restless, pulled up the stake, and went off, dragging stake and saddles! He waited another hour, with his heart going down and down. It was past noon. The horses were lying down. He took another drink, tightened his belt, and set forth on Deacon's tracks. They moved in curves, as of an S, as though he had been quartering the ground. He had followed them for half an hour, when the ground began to slope, and he suddenly caught sight of a dark object on the sand. In another hundred yards he made out Deacon, under his wide felt hat, sitting on the ground. The 'Cooee!' that burst from Cursitor's throat surprised him by its volume; he repeated it, hurrying along. Deacon made no sign. His back was turned, and he seemed gazing, motionless——over the sloping sand. Had he gone deaf, or out of his mind? Cursitor came up in anger.

"Deacon!" he said. The fellow was leaning slightly forward over his knees, a little black pipe in his hand, a little yellow dribble at the corner of his smiling lips; a film over his staring eyes. Cursitor bent over and shook the blue-shirted shoulder, then desisted in amazement at the look on that ecstatic face. Deacon raised his hand, moving it in slow half-circle; it was as if he pointed to a promised Land stretched out before him. He reeked of that peculiar herbal odour.

'God!' thought Cursitor: 'opium!'

For some minutes he was so overcome by dismay that he simply stood and stared. Then, in fright, he made a des-

perate effort to rouse Deacon out of that ecstatic coma.
No good! The fellow must come to of his own accord.
And, taking from his hand the little pipe, he sat down to
wait. He had no experience of opium. How long would
Deacon sit like that, dreaming his dreams? And what
would he be like when he came to? At first nothing but
disgust filled Cursitor's mind. It was as if the captain of a
ship were found dead-drunk in a storm, the colonel of a
regiment lolling on a sofa with a lady while his regiment
was in action. The fellow was in Paradise, and he himself
in torment! And yet there was something in that sick
ecstasy which slowly, very slowly affected Cursitor's heart.
Little doubt the chap was seeing his dream fulfilled—a
mirage of green crops and running rills, of trees, and grass,
and flowers and fruits—of all that water brings. The fellow had hunted over that vast sand-drift for the crack to
his underground river, and the line that he had left; hunted like a lost dog for its master till, at last convinced that
the sand had guarded its secret, the desert beaten him, he
had fallen exhausted in the heat, and turned, in his despairing disappointment, to the certain respite of an opium
dream. There before him in a few brief moments, out
of a little smoke, he could fashion all that he had lost, all
that would have taken years of anxiety and risk and effort,
even with water in that desert; out of the sand in a quarter of an hour he had created him a Garden of Eden, like
God before him; the green sweetness, the corn and wine
and oil—or at least the alfalfa and tomatoes—of redemp-
tion. He had made the desert bloom like a rose, just by
lifting hand to mouth, and drawing in the fumes of a
little black burning pellet. Who could blame a chap so
bitterly disappointed of his hopes—this poor devil who had
lived twenty years on the edge of an unscratched waste,
dreaming his dreams of making something out of it? And
then a doubt—a swift doubt. Had the fellow ever struck

that rift at all, ever brought his line up, ever dropped it into any rich underground river? Was not that all a pipe-dream too, so strong and seizing that it had destroyed perception of reality? Gazing intently at that yellow ecstatic face Cursitor thought: 'I shall never know for certain— never know whether I haven't been utterly spoofed by a man who didn't know that he was spoofing.' The thought was too wounding. Bad enough to be spoofed by a sand-storm, to have had for nothing this laborious, perilous experience, of which he would never be able to speak, for fear of being taken for a fool! The expression on the too small but Napoleonic features of Markham Mays came back to him. And he sat almost as still as Deacon, waiting for that look of ecstasy to die on the yellow face, for the dream to fade, as all dreams must, into the starkness of reality. Hour after hour he waited, while the sun heeled slowly over them. About four o'clock Deacon rolled over and slept like a log. Cursitor let him sleep. He was devoured by thirst and fear. Were the horses still where he had left them, or had they broken loose and gone off to the mules and water? Somehow he must get that fellow back before darkness came and covered their footmarks in the sand. When Deacon had slept two hours, he made his effort. It took him half an hour to get the fellow on his legs. They set forth arm in arm, and during all that hour-long stumble beside their footmarks in the deep sand, he never spoke, and Deacon only said one word:

"Water."

The sight of the horses lying quietly where they had been left was the keenest relief Cursitor had ever known. In touch, however distantly, with civilisation, his indignation and disgust revived. He would tell the fellow what he thought of him. He never did. Deacon looked so sick and miserable—he hadn't the heart.

They started at eight o'clock, Cursitor in front, the reins

loose on his horse's neck; the creature would know the
way. Deacon rode with his head down—a beaten man.
A queer, protective feeling rose in Cursitor. What would
one have done in Deacon's shoes? No better—not so well.
The night air filled his tired body; his spirits revived, but
spent themselves no more in invitations to the Public. They
dwelt endlessly on drinks, on baths, on the sea, and fel-
low-beings who did not dream, but lived sanely and made
money where the earth had been tamed. But when at last
the smoke from the black fella's brush-fire was in his nostrils, his eyes swept the paling sky and the desert stretching
to the bonfire of the dawn with a joy that had a sort of
ache in it, as if he were leaving something precious that
he would never see again—the earth where Man was not,
the waterless adventure of his life. . . .

V

LEANING over the taffrail of the S.S. *Orinoco* three months
later, Cursitor watched Vesuvius growing small. He had
not raised a penny. The "Rangoon W.W.W.T." had
made no appeal to Melbourne, Sydney, Adelaide, Brisbane
and Perth, and in the light of the Mediterranean sunset
there seemed nothing in front of him.

"Yes, sir," said a voice behind him, "as I was saying
last night, that Basque region simply stinks of copper. If
I could raise the money to unwater a mine I know of not
a hundred miles from Bilbao, I could make my fortune.
There's copper there, running up to seventeen and more
per cent, and easily worked."

"Oh!" said Cursitor: "How did it get flooded?"

They got off at Gibraltar.

1924.

A PATRIOT

THE other day I was told a true story, which I remember vaguely hearing or reading about during the war, but which is worth retelling for those who missed it, for it has certain valuable ironic implications and a sort of grandeur. It concerns one of those beings who, when they spy upon us, are known by that word of three letters, as offensive as any in the language, and when they spy for us are dignified by the expression "Secret Service," and looked on as heroes of at least second water.

You will recollect that when the war broke out, the fifteen hundred persons engaged in supplying Germany with information, mainly trivial and mostly erroneous, concerning our condition and arrangements, were all known by the authorities and were put out of action at a single swoop. From that moment there was not one discovered case of espionage by spies already resident in England when war was declared. There were, however, a few and, I am told, unimportant discovered cases of espionage by persons who developed the practice or went into England for the purpose, during the war. This story concerns one of the latter.

*　　*　　*　　*　　*

In August 1914 there was living in America a business man of German birth and American citizenship, called— let us say, for it was not his name—Lichtfelder, who had once been an officer in the German Army; a man of about fifty, of square and still military appearance, with rather short stiff hair, a straight back to his head, and a patriotic conscience too strong for his American citizenship. It was not long then before an American called Lightfield landed

in Genoa and emerged as Lichtfelder at the German headquarters of his old regiment, offering his services.

"No," they said to him, "you are no longer a young and
active man, and you are an American citizen. We are very
disappointed with our Secret Service in England; something seems to have gone wrong. You can be of much
greater service to the Fatherland if, having learned our
codes, you will go to England as an American citizen and
send us all the information you can acquire."

Lichtfelder's soul was with his old regiment; but, being a patriot, he consented. During the next two months
he made himself acquainted with all the tricks of his new
trade, took ship again at Genoa, and reappeared as Lightfield in the United States. Soon after this he sailed for
Liverpool, well stocked with business addresses and samples,
and supplied with his legitimate American passport in his
own American name.

*   *   *   *   *

He spent the first day of his "Secret Service" wandering
about the docks of a town which, in his view—if not in
that of other people—was a naval station of importance;
he also noted carefully the half-militarised appearance of
the khaki figures in the streets; and in the evening he
penned a business letter to a gentleman in Rotterdam, between the lines of which, devoted to the more enlightened
forms of—shall we say?—plumbing, he wrote down in
invisible ink all he had seen—such and such ships arrived
or about to sail; such and such "khaki" drilling or wandering about the streets; all of which had importance in his
view, if not in fact. He ended with the words: "Morgens
Dublin Lichtfelder," and posted the letter.

Now, unfortunately for this poor but simple patriot, there
was a young lady in the General Post Office who was
spending her days in opening all letters with suspected for-

eign addresses, and submitting them to the test for invisible
ink. To her joy—for she was weary at the dearth of that
useful commodity—between the lines of this commercial
screed, which purported to be concerned with the refinements of plumbing, out sprang the guilty ink. To a certain
Department were telephoned the incautious "Morgens Dublin Lichtfelder." Now, no alien in those days was suffered
to leave for Ireland save through a bottle-neck at Holy-
head. To the bottle-neck then went the message: "Did
man called Lichtfelder travel yesterday to Dublin?" The
answer came quickly: "American called Lightfield went
Dublin yesterday returned last night, is now on train for
Euston." At Euston our patriot, after precisely three days
of secret service, was arrested, and lodged wherever they
were then lodged.

"I am," he said, "an American citizen called Lightfield."

"That," said the British Cabinet, not without disagree-
ment, "makes a difference. You shall be tried by ordinary
process of law, and defended by counsel chosen by the
American Embassy at our expense, instead of by court
martial."

* * * * *

Speedily—for in those days the law's delays were short
—the American citizen called Lightfield, *alias* Lichtfelder,
was put on his trial for supplying information to the enemy; and for three days, at the Government's expense, a
certain eminent counsel gave the utmost of his wits to
preparing his defence. But a certain great advocate, whose
business it was to prosecute, had given the utmost of his
wits to considering with what question he should open his
cross-examination, since it is well known how important is
the first question; and there had come to him an inspiration.

"Mr. Lichtfelder," he said, fixedly regarding that upright figure in the dock, "tell me: have you not been an officer in the German Army?"

The hands of the American citizen went to his sides, and his figure stiffened. For hours he had been telling the Court how entirely concerned he was with business, giving his references, showing his samples, explaining that—as for the lines in invisible ink in this letter, which he admitted sending—well, it was simply that he had met a Dutch journalist on board the ship coming out, who had said to him: "You know, we can get no news at all, we neutrals—do send us *something*—not, of course, harmful to England, but *something* we can say." And he had sent it. Was it harmful? It was nothing but trifles he had sent. And now, at that first question, he was standing suddenly a little more erect, and—silent.

And the great advocate said:

"I won't press you now, Mr. Lichtfelder: we will go on to other matters. But I should like you to think that question over, because it is not only the first question that I ask you—it will also be the last."

*   *   *   *   *

And the Court adjourned, the cross-examination not yet over, with that question not yet asked again.

In the early morning of the following day, when the warder went to the cell of Lichtfelder, there, by his muffler, dangled his body from the grating. Beneath the dead feet the cell Bible had been kicked away; but since, with the stretching of the muffler, those feet had still been able to rest on the ground, the patriot had drawn them up, until he was choked to death. He had waited till the dawn, for on the cell slate was written this:

I am a soldier with rank I do not desire to mention
. . . I have had a fair trial of the United Kingdom. I

am not dying as a spy, but as a soldier. My fate I
stood as a man, but I can't be a liar and perjure myself. . . . What I have done I have done for my country. I shall express my thanks, and may the Lord bless
you all.

And from the ten lawyers—eight English and two
American—who, with me, heard the story told, there came,
as it were, one murmur: "Jolly fine!"

And so it was! .

1927.

TOLD BY THE SCHOOLMASTER

W E all remember still, I suppose, the singular beauty of the summer when the war broke out. I was then schoolmaster in a village on the Thames. Nearly fifty, with a game shoulder and extremely deficient sight, there was no question of my fitness for military service, and this, as with many other sensitive people, induced in me, I suppose, a mood abnormally receptive. The perfect weather, that glowing countryside, with corn harvest just beginning and the apples already ripening, the quiet nights trembling with moonlight and shadow and, in it all, this great horror launched and growing, the weazening of Europe deliber-ately undertaken, the death-warrant of millions of young men signed— Such summer loveliness walking hand in hand with murder thus magnified beyond conception was too piercingly ironical!

One of those evenings, towards the end of August, when the news of Mons was coming through, I left my house at the end of the village street and walked up towards the Downs. I have never known anything more entrancing than the beauty of that night. All was still and coloured like the bloom of dark grapes; so warm, so tremulous. A rush of stars was yielding to the moon fast riding up, and from the corn-stooks of that early harvest the shadows were stealing out. We had no daylight-saving then, and it was perhaps half-past nine when I passed two of my former scholars, a boy and a girl, standing silently at the edge of an old gravel pit opposite a beech clump. They looked up and gave me good evening. Passing on over the crest, I could see the unhedged fields to either hand; the corn stooked and the corn standing, just gilded under the moon; the swelling Downs of a blue-grey; and the beech clump I had passed dark-cut against the brightening sky. The

moon itself was almost golden, as if it would be warm to
the touch, and from it came a rain of glamour over sky
and fields, woods, downs, farm-houses and the river down
below. All seemed in a conspiracy of unreality to one
obsessed, like me, by visions of the stark and trampling
carnage going on out there. Refuging from that grim comparison, I remember thinking that Jim Beckett and Betty
Roofe were absurdly young to be sweethearting, if indeed
they were, for they hadn't altogether looked like it. They
could hardly be sixteen yet, for they had only left school
last year. Betty Roofe had been head of the girls; an interesting child, alert, self-contained, with a well-shaped,
dark-eyed little face and a head set on very straight. She
was the daughter of the village laundress, and I used to
think too good for washing clothes, but she was already at
it and, as things went in that village, would probably go on
doing it till she married. Jim Beckett was working on
Carver's farm down there below me and the gravel pit was
about half-way between their homes. A good boy, Jim,
freckled, reddish in the hair and rather too small in the
head; with blue eyes that looked at you very straight, and
a short nose; a well-grown boy, very big for his age, and
impulsive in spite of the careful stodginess of all young
rustics; a curious vein of the sensitive in him, but a great
deal of obstinacy, too—altogether an interesting blend!

I was still standing there when up he came on his way to
Carver's and I look back to that next moment with as much
regret as to any in my life.

He held out his hand.

"Good-bye, sir, in case I don't see you again."

"Why, where are you off to, Jim?"

"Joinin' up."

"Joining up? But, my dear boy, you're two years under
age, at least."

He grinned. "I'm sixteen this month, but I bet I can

make out to be eighteen. They ain't particular, I'm told."

I looked him up and down. It was true, he could pass for eighteen well enough, with military needs what they were. And possessed, as everyone was just then, by patriotism and anxiety at the news, all I said was:

"I don't think you ought, Jim; but I admire your spirit."

He stood there silent, sheepish at my words. Then:

"Well, good-bye, sir. I'm goin' to ——ford to-morrow."

I gave his hand a good hard squeeze. He grinned again, and without looking back, ran off down the hill towards Carver's farm, leaving me alone once more with the unearthly glamour of that night. God! what a crime was war! From this hushed moonlit peace boys were hurrying off to that business of man-made death as if there were not Nature's deaths galore to fight against. And we—we could only admire them for it! Well! I have never ceased to curse the sentiment which stopped me from informing the recruiting authorities of that boy's real age.

Crossing back over the crest of the hill towards home I came on the child Betty, at the edge of the gravel pit where I had left her.

"Well, Betty, was Jim telling you?"

"Yes, sir; he's going to join up."

"What did you say to him?"

"I said he was a fool, but he's so headstrong, Jim!" Her voice was even enough, but she was quivering all over.

"It's very plucky of him, Betty."

"M'm! Jim just gets things into his head. I don't see that he has any call to go and—and leave me."

I couldn't help a smile. She saw it, and said sullenly:

"Yes, I'm young, and so's Jim; but he's my boy, for all that!"

And then, ashamed or startled at such expansiveness, she tossed her head, swerved into the beech clump like a shying foal, and ran off among the trees. I stood a few minutes, listening to the owls, then went home and read myself into forgetfulness on Scott's first Polar book.

So Jim went and we knew him no more for a whole year. And Betty continued with her mother washing for the village.

II

In September, 1915, just after term had begun again, I was standing one afternoon in the village schoolroom pinning up on the wall a pictorial piece of imperial information for the benefit of my scholars, and thinking, as usual, of the war, and its lingering deadlock. The sunlight slanted through on to my dusty forms and desks, and under the pollard lime-trees on the far side of the street I could see a soldier standing with a girl. Suddenly he crossed over to the school, and there in the doorway was young Jim Beckett in his absurd short-tailed khaki jacket, square and tanned to the colour of his freckles, looking, indeed, quite a man.

"How d'you do, sir?"

"And you, Jim?"

"Oh, I'm fine! I thought I'd like to see you. Just got our marching orders. Off to France to-morrow; been havin' my leave."

I felt the catch at my throat that we all felt when youngsters whom we knew were going out for the first time.

"Was that Betty with you out there?"

"Yes—fact is, I've got something to tell you, sir. She and I were spliced last week at ——mouth. We been stayin' there since, and I brought her home to-day, as I got to go to-night."

I was staring hard, and he went on hurriedly:

"She just went off there and I joined her for my leave.

We didn't want any fuss, you see, because of our bein' too young."

"Young!"

The blankness of my tone took the grin off his face.

"Well, I was seventeen a week ago and she'll be seventeen next month."

"Married? Honest Injun, Jim?"

He went to the door and whistled. In came Betty, dressed in dark blue, very neat and self-contained; only the flush on her round young face marked any disturbance.

"Show him your lines, Betty, and your ring."

The girl held out the official slip and from it I read that a registrar had married them at ———mouth, under right names and wrong ages.

Then she slipped a glove off and held up her left hand —there was the magic hoop! Well! the folly was committed; no use in crabbing it!

"Very good of you to tell me, Jim," I said at last. "Am I the first to know?"

"Yes, sir. You see, I've got to go at once, and like as not her mother won't want it to get about till she's a bit older. I thought I'd like to tell *you*, in case they said it wasn't all straight and proper."

"Nothing I say will alter the fact that you've falsified your ages."

Jim grinned again.

"That's all right," he said. "I got it from a lawyer's clerk in my platoon. It's a marriage all the same."

"Yes; I believe that's so."

"Well, sir, there she is till I come back." Suddenly his face changed; he looked for all the world as if he were going to cry; and they stood gazing at each other exactly as if they were alone.

The lodger at the carpenter's, three doors down the street, was performing her usual afternoon solo on the

piano, *"Connais-tu le pays?"* from *Mignon*. And whenever I hear it now, seldom enough in days contemptuous of
harmony, it brings Jim and Betty back through a broad
sunbeam full of dancing motes of dust; it epitomises for
me all the *Drang*—as the Germans call it—of those horrible years, when marriage, birth, death and every human
activity were speeded up to their limit, and we did from
year's end to year's end all that an enlightened humanity
should not be doing, and left undone most of what it should
have done.

"What time is it, sir?" Jim asked me suddenly.

"Five o'clock."

"Lord! I must run for it. My kit's at the station.
Could I leave her here, sir?"

I nodded and walked into the little room beyond. When
I came back she was sitting where she used to sit in school,
bowed over her arms spread out on the inky desk. Her dark
bobbed hair was all I could see, and the quivering jerky
movement of her young shoulders. Jim had gone. Well!
That was the normal state of Europe, then! I went back
into the little room to give her time, but when I returned
once more she, too, had gone.

III

THE second winter passed, more muddy, more bloody
even than the first, and less shot through with hopes of
an ending. Betty showed me three or four of Jim's letters,
simple screeds with a phrase here and there of awkward
and half-smothered feeling, and signed always "Your loving hubby, Jim." Her marriage was accepted in the village.
Child-marriage was quite common then. In April it began
to be obvious that their union was to be "blessed," as they
call it.

One day early in May I was passing Mrs. Roofe's when I saw that lady in her patch of garden, and stopped to ask after Betty.

"Nearin' her time. I've written to Jim Beckett. Happen he'll get leave."

"I think that was a mistake, Mrs. Roofe. I would have waited till it was over."

"Maybe you're right, sir; but Betty's that fidgety about him not knowin'. She's dreadful young, you know, t' 'ave a child. I didn't 'ave my first till I was twenty-one."

"Everything goes fast these days, Mrs. Roofe."

"Not my washin'. I can't get the help, with Betty like this. It's a sad business this about the baby comin'. If he does get killed I suppose she'll get a pension, sir?"

Pension? Married in the wrong age, with the boy still under service age, if they came to look into it. I really didn't know.

"Oh, surely, Mrs. Roofe! But we won't think about his being killed. Jim's a fine boy."

Mrs. Roofe's worn face darkened.

"He was a fool to join up before his time; plenty of chance after, seemingly; and then to marry my girl like this! Well, young folk *are* fools!"

I was sitting over my Pensions work one evening, a month later, for it had now fallen to me to keep things listed in the village, when someone knocked at my door, and who should be standing there but Jim Beckett!

"Why! Jim! Got leave?"

"Ah! I had to come and see her. I haven't been there yet; didn' dare. How is she, sir?"

Pale and dusty, as if from a hard journey, his uniform all muddy and unbrushed, and his reddish hair standing up anyhow——he looked wretched, poor boy!

"She's all right, Jim. But it must be very near, from what her mother says."

"I haven't had any sleep for nights, thinking of her—such a kid, she is!"

"Does she know you re coming?"

"No, I haven't said nothing."

"Better be careful. I wouldn't risk a shock. Have you anywhere to sleep?"

"No, sir."

"Well, you can stay here if you like. They won't have room for you there." He seemed to back away from me.

"Thank ye, sir. I wouldn' like to put you out."

"Not a bit, Jim; delighted to have you and hear your adventures."

He shook his head. "I don't want to talk of them," he said darkly. "Don't you think I could see 'er to-night, sir? I've come a long way for it, my God! I have!"

"Well, try! But see her mother first."

"Yes, sir," and he touched his forehead. His face, so young a face, already had that look in the eyes of men who stare death down.

He went away and I didn't see him again that night. They had managed, apparently, to screw him into their tiny cottage. He was only just in time, for two days later Betty had a boy-child. He came to me the same evening, after dark, very excited.

"She's a wonder," he said; "but if I'd known I'd never ha' done it, sir, I never would. You can't tell what you're doing till it's too late, it seems."

Strange saying from that young father, till afterwards it was made too clear!

Betty recovered quickly and was out within three weeks.

Jim seemed to have long leave, for he was still about, but I had little talk with him, for, though always friendly, he seemed shy of me, and as to talking of the war—not a word! One evening I passed him and Betty leaning on a gate, close to the river—a warm evening of early July,

when the Somme battle was at its height. Out there hell
incarnate; and here intense peace, the quietly flowing river,
the willows, and unstirring aspens, the light slowly dying,
and those two young things, with their arms round each
other and their heads close together——her bobbed dark hair
and Jim's reddish mop, getting quite long! I took good
care not to disturb them. His last night, perhaps, before he
went back into the furnace!

*   *   *   *   *

It was no business of mine to have my doubts, but I had
been having them long before that very dreadful night
when, just as I was going to bed, something rattled on my
window, and going down I found Betty outside, distracted.

"Oh, sir, come quick! They've 'rested Jim."

As we went over she told me:

"Oh, sir, I was afraid there was some mistake about his
leave——it was so long; I thought he'd get into trouble over
it, so I asked Bill Pateman"——(the village constable)——
"and now they've come and 'rested him for deserting. Oh!
What have I done? What have I done?"

Outside the Roofes' cottage Jim was standing between
a corporal's guard, and Betty flung herself into his arms.
Inside I could hear Mrs. Roofe expostulating with the corporal, and the baby crying. In the sleeping quiet of the
village street, smelling of hay just harvested, it was atroci-
ous.

I spoke to Jim. He answered quietly, in her arms:

"I asked for leave, but they wouldn't give it. I had to
come. I couldn't stick it, knowing how it was with her."

"Where was your regiment?"

"In the line."

"Good God!"

Just then the corporal came out. I took him apart.

"I was his schoolmaster, Corporal," I said. "The poor

chap joined up when he was just sixteen—he's still under age, you see; and now he's got this child-wife and a new-born baby!"

The corporal nodded; his face was twitching, a lined, decent face with a moustache.

"I know, sir," he muttered. "I know. Cruel work, but I've got to take him. He'll have to go back to France."

"What does it mean?"

He lifted his arms from his sides and let them drop, and that gesture was somehow the most expressive and dreadful I ever saw.

"Deserting in face of the enemy," he whispered hoarsely. "Bad business! Can you get that girl away, sir?"

But Jim himself undid the grip of her arms and held her from him. Bending, he kissed her hair and face, then, with a groan, he literally pushed her into my arms and marched straight off between the guard.

And I was left in the dark, sweet-scented street with that distracted child struggling in my grasp.

"Oh, my God! My God! My God!" Over and over and over. And what could one say or do?

IV

ALL the rest of that night, after Mrs. Roofe had got Betty back into the cottage, I sat up writing in duplicate the facts about Jim Beckett. I sent one copy to his regimental headquarters, the other to the chaplain of his regiment in France. I sent fresh copies two days later with duplicates of his birth certificates to make quite sure. It was all I could do. Then came a fortnight of waiting for news. Betty was still distracted. The thought that, through her anxiety, she herself had delivered him into their hands nearly sent her off her head. Probably her baby alone kept her from insanity, or suicide. And all that time the battle of the Somme raged and hundreds of thousands of women in England and France and Germany were in daily terror for their menfolk. Yet none, I think, could have had quite the feeling of that child. Her mother, poor woman, would come over to me at the schoolhouse and ask if I had heard anything.

"Better for the poor girl to know the worst," she said, "if it is the worst. The anxiety's killin' 'er."

But I had no news and could not get any at headquarters. The thing was being dealt with in France. Never was the scale and pitch of the world's horror more brought home to me. This deadly little tragedy was as nothing—just a fragment of straw whirling round in that terrible wind.

And then one day I did get news—a letter from the chaplain—and seeing what it was I stuck it in my pocket and sneaked down to the river—literally afraid to open it till I was alone. Crouched up there, with my back to a haystack, I took it out with trembling fingers.

"Dear Sir,

"The boy Jim Beckett was shot to-day at dawn. I am distressed at having to tell you and the poor child his wife. War is a cruel thing indeed."

I had known it. Poor Jim! Poor Betty! Poor, poor Betty! I read on:

"I did all I could; the facts you sent were put before the Court Martial and the point of his age considered. But all leave had been stopped; his request had been definitely refused; the regiment was actually in the line, with fighting going on—and the situation extremely critical in that sector. Private considerations count for nothing in such circumstances—the rule is adamant. Perhaps it has to be—

I cannot say. But I have been greatly distressed by the whole thing, and the Court itself was much moved. The poor boy seemed dazed; he wouldn't talk; didn't seem to take in anything; indeed, they tell me that all he said after the verdict, certainly all I heard him say was: 'My poor wife! My poor wife!' over and over again. He stood up well at the end."

He stood up well at the end! I can see him yet, poor impulsive Jim. Desertion, but not cowardice, by the Lord! No one who looked into those straight, blue eyes could believe that. But they bandaged them, I suppose. Well! a bullet in a billet more or less; what was it in that whole-sale slaughter? As a raindrop on a willow tree drips into the river and away to sea—so that boy, like a million others, dripped to dust. A little ironical though, that his own side should shoot him, who went to fight for them two years before he need, to shoot him who wouldn't be legal food for powder for another month! A little ironical, perhaps, that he had left this son—legacy to such an implacable world! But there's no moral to a true tale like this—unless it be that the rhythm of life and death cares not a jot for any of us!

1925.

THE SMILE

M^R. JUSTICE BELLIVER sat in the armchair of his
retiring-room, at close of his day's work, twisting up
one of his still dark eyebrows between thumb and finger.
He usually sat for ten minutes in this manner, reviewing
the case in hand before throwing it off his mind till after
dinner. His other hand, thin with darkish hair on it,
rubbed his pepper and salt knees without seeming purpose.
About sixty-five, and if not handsome, at least impressive,
he still had on his face the somewhat dehumanised look of
the last six hours. Owing to pressure of divorce, he had
been dissolving marriages all the week—not his general
game, and rather enjoyable for a change; but to-day there
was a point of irritation in his mind, such as a hair un-
located causes in a mouth. He had just pronounced *decree
nisi* in a suit where Counsel had made an appeal that, in
spite of her guilt, the respondent should be allowed to keep
the child of the marriage. In his judgment he had made it
plain that no talk of temptation, no throwing of blame on
the co-respondent, was to the point; she was a married
woman who had been false to her vows, and he had felt
no hesitation in following the usual practice, giving custody
of the child to the party not in error.

He had no doubt about his judgment, yet was uneasy,
because he could not put his finger on that vague spot of
irritation. His mental eye reviewed the figures of the
parties: petitioner, cold, well-dressed; respondent, perhaps
twenty-six, slim, pretty, fair-haired, seated beside a tall,
large woman in black with a full-blown face, evidently
her mother.

He rose impatiently, and, going to a drawer, took out
some brushes and began brushing his grey hair.

Ah! Somebody had smiled while he was delivering

judgment—a sort of contempt of Court. His tongue had found the hair. But who—where——? In the gallery—body of the Court—Counsel's bench? No! Ah! That woman with the full-blown face—the mother! Hardly the moment for a mother——! His mental eye isolated the smile on those full lips, in those swimming blue eyes; it had a queer, concentrated meaning, a sort of threatening quizzicality—altogether a piece of infernal impertinence! If it had occurred again, he would have had the Court cleared of—h'm—well!

He opened his toilet cabinet and washed his face and hands, as if rubbing off a smear. Then, taking his top hat, with a few words to his attendant, he made his way out of the Law Courts. It was fine, and, beckoning up his chauffeur, he sent his car away.

While he was turning out of Lincoln's Inn Fields into Long Acre, a closed car passed him, moving very slowly. Mr. Justice Belliver looked up. The window space was filled by a lady's face under a large black hat. So slowly the car moved, that for half a minute the face, full-blown, with blue swimming eyes, was turned towards him, and on the face that smile. It seemed to travel up and down him, to quiz him from the soles of his boots to the top of his hat; it rested on his angry eyes, burrowed, dug into them with a clinging devilry, annoying, puzzling him so intensely that he could not take his eyes off it. Men's glances are supposed sometimes to divest women of their clothes; this woman's smile divested Mr. Justice Belliver, not exactly of his clothes, but of his self-possession, self-importance, almost of his self-control. He was ashamed to stop, turn round, or cross the road, he just walked and stood it, getting very red; and all the time he could see that the woman was extremely pleased with the effect. Then the car suddenly speeded, and he was alone, using an unjudicial word.

What was the meaning of it? He racked his brains to

remember her name—mentioned in the case; Mac—Mac
—something—quite unfamiliar to him; and her face—no
—unless—no, quite unknown!

Again he used the unjudicial word, and with the power
that his life had given him, turned his mind to other things
—almost.

Before taking his seat in Court next morning, he perused
the shorthand report of the case; the names conveyed
nothing to him. Towards lunch-time, while he was pro-
nouncing his second *decree nisi*, his eyes, roving over the
Court, were arrested by a large black hat in the front row
of the gallery. Beneath it—yes!—that woman's face, and
smiling! The impudence! By heaven! he would have her
removed! Removed? He lowered his eyes, broke a nib
angrily against his desk, and with an effort finished his
judgment and adjourned the Court.

He sat before his lunch without eating, very angry. At
that distance, the smile, endowed as if with enchantment,
had been more irritating, baffling, damnably quizzing than
ever. It was such contempt of Court as he had never
known; yet what could he do? He was exposed to her impudence whenever he sat in public, so long as she might
wish. It was absurd! And yet—there was something behind—some cursed meaning that he could not reach. Had
he said anything foolish in his judgment yesterday? He
took up the report a second time. No! Nothing but what
he would say again this minute; he agreed with every word
of it! Well, if he couldn't commit her for contempt of
Court, he must ignore her.

He attacked his risotto, nearly cold by now, drank his
glass of claret, put on his wig, and again went into Court.

When Counsel sat down after opening the new case, he
saw in the gap made by the dropping of the gowned figure,
that woman under her large black hat—smiling, with the
same meaning devilry, the same quizzing, burrowing em-

phasis, on his face. His stare, fierce for a moment, became grim and stony. He leaned back, gripping his chair with both hands. He had been on the very point of saying: "If a certain person in Court cannot behave with the respect due to Justice, I shall have her removed."

Phew! What an escape! This was a question of will-power! Was a woman going to beat him at that? If she was bent on a petty persecution, well—one would see! And one did. For whenever his eyes in the business of the case were raised, there was that woman's face, there was that smile.

Not even after influenza had it been so great a strain to keep his mind on the business of the Court. When at last he adjourned, he beckoned the usher. He would point out the woman; give instructions for her exclusion.

"Yes, my Lord?"

"The ventilation was not all it might be this afternoon. See to it, will you?"

"Yes, my Lord."

And my Lord rose, and as he rose, the woman rose, and smiled.

Driving home that day, he sat back with closed eyes. Not a particularly unimaginative man, he was unimaginative enough to see that he was making a fool of himself. The woman was revenging herself for his judgment about her daughter's child, but if a judge had not the strength of mind to disregard such petty persecutions, he was not fit for his job! He smiled best, anyway, who smiled last! Yet, racking his brains for a way of smiling last, he could not find one.

Next morning he forced himself at once to scrutinise every corner of the Court. No woman! She did not appear. The next day was Sunday. By Monday morning the matter had almost passed from his mind, leaving the unpleasant dent of a sinister dream. He was back in the

King's Bench, too, with his old work; and surely no woman would put up with the boredom of Common Law cases for the pleasure of annoying him.

But her smile was almost the first thing he saw when he entered, and he was alarmed by its effect. Consciousness that it was ready to pounce the moment his eyes strayed, seemed to deprive him of all that serenity, so necessary for the trial of Common Law cases.

And the next day it was the same, and the next.

Sitting in his Club that third evening before dinner, he reviewed the courses open to him to abate the nuisance. Only a fortnight to the Easter vacation, but a fortnight of such daily irritation would make him ill. The idea of having her removed, or committed for contempt of Court, did not seriously return to him—too like the Red King in *Alice in Wonderland;* and what if, like the Cheshire Cat, she left her smile behind—for not so much the woman now, as what her smile meant, was on his nerves. Some meaning—and he could not reach it! What courses then were left? To go to the woman's home and confront her? Impossible! Dignity of office forbade.

Write? Equally undignified!

Go sick and begin his vacation at once? That would leave her with the victory!

Get a friend to interfere? No! He could not confide his weakness to a friend.

Take to smoked glasses? They would but blur his view of counsel and witnesses, and leave the smile undimmed; for, now, it was a "haunt," too mental in effect to be removed that way. Besides—the woman would see them and comprehend!

Laugh—at himself, at her! Yes, if it were just a revengeful trick. But how laugh at what one could not understand?

He rose from that session of sweet, silent thought, powerless, devoid of remedy, of anodyne. One must just stick it out and trust to time to wear the woman down. And with a deep sigh he went in to dinner.

The woman missed no single one of the ten days that followed; for two or three hours, morning or afternoon, she sat in his Court and smiled whenever he gave her a chance; and that was often, for when a rider has a weak spot, out of sheer nervousness he always falls on it.

He had almost lost consciousness of how the thing began; it was as unreal, and yet as painful, as a recurrent nightmare. When he adjourned his Court for the Easter vacation, his face had a jaundiced look, his eyes were restless and unhappy, his dark, twisting eyebrows had lost their attractive stiver. And the woman looked as fresh, full-blown, meaningful, and mocking as on the first day he saw her. She had battened on him.

Never had he entered train for his vacation with such intense relief. Brighton air would set him up, remove this silly nerve-exasperation. By Croydon already he felt soothed; by Three Bridges his fighting instinct had returned—he was a man again. He drove up to his hotel with the buoyant feeling of a man out for the first time after an illness. In the hall lounge, he passed two ladies. One of them turned and smiled. For a moment, he felt positively faint; then with the thought: "Ha! but I'm not a judge here!" he stepped up to the bureau and registered his name. Here she was no privileged harpy, he no helpless official butt—he was a man—and she should know it!

Before dinner he had matured a resolve to dog her to some quiet nook and give her the half-hour of her life.

"Madam," he would begin, "I have reason to know your face. You have been so good as to favour me with certain smiles these last three weeks." By Heaven! his tongue should tear the skin off her!

In the coffee-room he searched every table, looked at

every face; she was not there. Perhaps she had inkling, had repented of her rashness in pursuing him down here.

After dinner he continued his restless search, but he could not see her anywhere, and at last sat down in the lounge, where a screen kept off the draught, and lay back in his chair drawing feebly at his cigar. Unnerved, exhausted by this spurt of savage feeling, he dozed off.

He was awakened by voices. Two women were talking somewhere close to him.

"And he doesn't know me from Eve—isn't it priceless! My dear, I've had the time of my life. From the moment he said that Kathleen shouldn't have the child, sneered at her, wouldn't have it that Charles pursued her, I made up my mind to get back on him. He—*he*—of all men! Why, do you know that twenty-seven years ago, in my first marriage, when I was twenty-three, slim and pretty as an angel —my dear, I was, though you mightn't think it—he—*he* —a barrister he was then, and quite a buck—made violent love to me; even wanted me to go off with him. And I should have, my dear, if it hadn't been that Kathleen was on the way! *He*—*he!* He's clean forgotten that he ever was flesh and blood! And now! Oh, my God! *What* a humbug! What a humbug, in his precious wig! Hallo!"

The screen was tottering. Mr. Justice Belliver, risen from his hastily pushed-back chair, with one hand grasped the falling screen, with the other the lapel of his evening coat, as if to conceal the feelings in his chest. His lips quivered, bloodless from compression; with eyes very deep in his head, he stood looking at the woman who had spoken, and as he looked she smiled.

He bowed slightly, let go of the screen, walked shakily away; in a mirror he saw her smile slowly fading, and a look of compunction, almost of compassion, take its place.

1922.

THE BLACK COAT

THE old general, *émigré*, and member of the old-time
Russian nobility, who had commanded a division in
the Great War, sat on a crazy chair before a feeble fire in
his garret in the heart of Europe. His thin, high-shouldered form was crouched forward and his bluish hands
extended to what there was of flame, for he was seventy,
and his blood thin and cold. It had rained on his way back
from the Russian friends whom every Sunday evening he
went to see, and his coat was carefully spread out to dry,
over the back of his one other crazy chair, before the poor
conflagration in the grate.

It was the General's custom to light a fire on Sunday
evenings, when it was at all financially possible; the ceremony prolonged, with its apology for warmth, the three
hours per week during which he wore the clothes of a gentleman, in the society of gentlefolk. And he would sit
before it in his one suit—very old now and white about the
seams, but still modish in essence—smoking what of tobacco
he had brought away with him, and thinking of the past.
The present he never thought of at such times; it did not
bear the process, for his present, day by day, consisted in
walking before a dustman's cart, ringing a bell to announce
its coming to the inhabitants of the street; and for this he
received so little that he was compelled also, to keep soul
within body, to wash omnibuses in a garage near by. These
avocations provided him with the rent of his garret and
two meals a day; and while engaged in them he wore
dingy overalls which had once been blue, and took his two
meals at a workmen's café. On Sundays he stayed in bed
till evening, when he would rise, wash and shave himself
with slow and meticulous care; then, donning his old black

coat and carefully creased trousers, would go forth and
walk the two miles to the flat of his friends, where he was
sure of a meal and a little wine or vodka, and could talk
of the old Russia.

This is what he had been doing for fifty-two weeks in
the year during the past five years, and what he counted on
doing for the rest of his natural life. How he gained his
living was perfectly well known to his friends, but since it
was never spoken of by him, none of them would have considered it decent to mention it. Indeed, on those Sunday
evenings there was a tacit agreement not to speak of one's
misfortunes. Old Russia, politics, and the spirit of man
held the field, together with such other topics as were suit-
able to a black coat. And not infrequently there would
rise, above the ground bass droning through the lives of
émigrés, the gallantry of laughter. His friends themselves,
and all their guests, had the dark cupboards of the outcast
and the fallen, and gleaming skeletons within them; and
so it was essential that neither by word, by manner, nor by
dress, should the existence of an evil fate be admitted.
You might talk of restoration, of redress, of revenge, but
of daily need and pressure—no! And in truth there was
not much talk of the three R's; rather did conversation ape
normality.

And none was so normal as the old General. His was a
single mind, a simple face intensely stamped with wrinkles,
like the wrigglings in the texture of old pale leather which
is stained here and there a little darker by chance misusage.
He had folds in the lids over his rimmed brown eyes, a grey
moustache clung close round the corners of his bloodless
lips, and grey hair grew fairly low still on his square forehead. High-shouldered, he would stand with his head po-
litely inclined, taking in the talk, just, as now, before his
meagre fire, he seemed taking in the purr and flutter of the
flames.

After such evenings of talk, indeed, his memory would step with a sort of busy idleness into the past, as might a person in a garden of familiar flowers and trees; and, with the saving instinct of memory, would choose the grateful experiences of a life which, like most soldiers' lives, had marked a great deal of time, and been feverishly active in the intervals. The Czar's stamp was on his soul; for, after a certain age, no matter what the cataclysm, there can be no real change in the souls of men. The General might ring his dustman's bell and wash his casual omnibuses and eat the fare of workmen, but all such daily efforts were as a dream of dismal quality. Only in his black coat, as it were, was he awake. It could be said with truth that all the life he now lived was passed on Sunday evenings between the hours of six and midnight.

And now, with the smoke of his friend's cigar—for he always brought one away with him; no great shakes, but still a cigar—to lull reality and awaken the past, he smiled faintly, as might some old cat reflecting on a night out, and with all the Russian soul of him savoured the moment so paradoxically severed from the present. To go to his lean bed on Sunday nights was ever the last thing he wished to do, and he would put it off and off until the fire was black, and often fall asleep there and wake up in the small hours, shivering. He had so much that was pleasant in the past to think of every Sunday evening, after those hours spent in his black coat among his own kind had enlivened the soul within him, it was no wonder that he prolonged that séance to the last gasp of warmth.

To-night he was particularly absent from the present, for a young girl had talked to him who reminded him of an affair he had had in 1880, when he was in garrison in the Dnieper country. Her name he had forgotten, but not the kisses she had given him in return for nothing but his own; nor the soft, quizzical and confiding expression on

her roseleaf-coloured, rather flat-nosed face, nor her eyes
like forget-me-nots. The night his regiment got its orders
and he left her——what a night! The fruit trees white with
blossom, someone singing, and the moon hanging low on
the far side of the wide river. Heh, heh! the Russian land
——the wide, the calm, sweet-scented Russian land!

And the history that centred round that river, of the
Zaporogis——he used to know it well, with his passion for
military history, like that of most young men! A scent of
nettles, of burdock, of the leaves on young birch trees,
seemed mysteriously conveyed to him in his garret, and he
could see lilac——lilac and acacias, flowering in front of
flat, low houses; and the green cupolas of churches, away
in the dips of the plain, and the turned earth black. Holy
Russia! Ah! and that mare he had of the hook-nosed gipsy
at Ekaterinoslav——he had never seen the equal of her black
shining coat——what a jewel of a mare!

The cigar burned his lips and he threw the tiny stump
into the ashes. That fire was going out——damp wood! But
he had a little petrol from the garage in an old medicine
bottle. He would cheer the wood up. His coat wasn't dry
yet——a heavy rain to-night! He got the bottle and spar-
ingly dripped its contents on the smouldering wood——his
hand shook nowadays, and he spilled a little. Then he sat
down again, and the Burg clock struck twelve. Little
flames were creeping out now! Little memories creeping
to him from them! How those Japanese had fought! And
how his men went through the wood, the day he got his
cross. A wall——a Russian wall——great fellows! "Lead us,
little father——we will take the wood!" And he had led
them. Two bullets through his thigh that day, and a wipe
on the left shoulder! That was a life!

The crazy chair creaked, and he sidled back in it——if
one leaned forward, the old chair might break, and that
wouldn't do! No chair to sit on then. A cat's weight

would break down that on which his coat was spread. And he was drowsy now! He would dream nicely with that fine blaze. A great evening—the young girl had talked—talked —a pretty little hand to kiss! God bless all warmth! . . . And the General, in his crazy chair, slept, while the fire crept forward on the trickled petrol. From the streets below, too narrow for any car, came up no sound, and through the uncurtained window the stars were bright. Rain must have ceased—frost must be coming. And there was silence in the room, for the General could not snore, his chin was pressed too hard against his chest. He slept like a traveller who has made a long journey. And in the Elysian fields of his past he still walked in his dreams, and saw the flowering, and the flow of waters, the birds and the maidens and the beasts inhabiting.

Two hours passed and he woke up with a sneeze. Something was tickling his nose. Save for starshine it was dark —the fire out. He rose and groped for his matches and a bit of candle. He must be up in time to ring his bell before the dust-cart; and, neatly folding his precious trousers, he crept under his two blankets, wrinkling his nose, full of a nasty, bitter smell!

A soldier's habit of waking when he would, rang its silent alarm at seven o'clock. Cold! A film of ice had gathered on the water in his cracked ewer—but, to precede a dust-cart one need not wash too carefully! He had finished and was ready to go forth, when he remembered his black coat. One must fold and put it away with the camphor and dried lavender in the old trunk. He took it hastily from the back of the crazy chair, and his heart stood still. What was this? A great piece of it in the middle of the back, just where the tails were set on, crumbled in his hands—scorched—scorched to tinder! The wreck dangled in his grip like a corpse from a gibbet. Great God! His coat—his old black coat! Ruined past repair. He stood there quite motionless. It meant—what did it mean? And suddenly, down the leathery yellow of his cheeks, two tears rolled slowly. His old coat; his one coat! In all the weeks of all these years he had never been able to buy a garment, never been able to put by a single stiver. And, dropping the ruined coat, as one might drop the hand of a friend who had played one a dirty trick, he staggered from the room and down the stairs. The smell—that bitter smell! The smell of scorching gone stale!

In front of the dust-cart, in his dingy jeans, ringing his bell, he walked through the streets of the old city like a man in a bad dream. In the café he ate his bit of bread and sausage, drank his poor coffee, smoked his one cigarette. His mind refused to dwell on his misfortune. Only when washing an omnibus that evening in the garage he stopped suddenly, as if choked. The smell of the petrol had caught him by the throat—petrol that had been the ruin of his coat.

So passed that week, and Sunday came. He did not get up at all, but turned his face to the wall instead. He tried his best, but the past would not come to him. It needed the better food, the warming of the little wine, the talk, the scent of tobacco, the sight of friendly faces. And holding his grey head tight in his hands, he ground his teeth. For only then he realised that he was no longer alive; that all his soul had been in those few Sunday evening hours, when, within the shelter of his black coat, he refuged in the past. Another, and another week! His friends were all so poor. A soldier of old Russia—a general—well-born—he made no sign to them; he could not beg and he did not complain. But he had ceased to live, and he knew it, having no longer any past to live for. And something Russian in his soul—something uncompromising and extreme—something which refused to blink fact, and went with hand out-stretched to meet Fate—hardened and grew within him.

The rest is a paragraph from a journal:

"The body of an old grey-haired man was taken from the river this morning. The indications point to suicide, and the cast of features would suggest that another Russian *émigré* has taken Fate into his own hands. The body was clothed in trousers, shirt and waistcoat of worn but decent quality; it had no coat."

1926.

THE MUMMY

IN the end shelter of that Devon watering-place, Eugene Daunt had been sitting for two days and nights. At sixty-three, and with his lack of adipose, any but the southwest wind in late October must have "sewn him up" long before. He sat, huddled in his worn blue overcoat with belt tight-drawn, peaked golfing cap over his eyes, and his skinny brown hands deep-thrust into his pockets—dozing or staring before him. This end shelter was out of range of lamplight, and few passed it even in the daytime. For these reasons he had chosen it. He had ceased to wonder how much longer he could "stick it." His nodding thoughts were free from the tortures of effort. The cards were hopelessly against him, and he just wanted to be let alone. Nothing so definite as suicide was in his drowsing mind. Suicide meant effort, and he had always avoided effort, except in the playing of games. He played this last game—conserving the ebbing vitality of his body, ribby as a greyhound's. Neither was he bitter, sitting there. Natural that the "Johnnies," of whom he had borrowed scantily these last five years, should be "fed-up." He would have been "fed-up" himself. Natural that his old landlady should have come to him crying—"poor old soul"; a wonder she hadn't, long ago. He had shifted two watering-places down the coast, to sit it out where he was not known. On his lean brown face lurked a sort of grin. He looked a little like a Red Indian: had there ever been one who needed their stoicism more—or needed it less?

Only child of an Indian civilian, Eugene Daunt had been born in India, and taken home at the age of five. While at a private school he lost both parents—killed in an accident, and fell under the protection of his father's sister,

an unmarried lady, who lived at Baymouth, in the West
Country, and doted on him. He passed on to a public
school, where he remained till he was seventeen.

He was given to dyspepsia, but apt at games; good-look-
ing, assured, stoical; he won races, made scores; had indi-
gestion whenever there was an examination. It was thought
that he would go into the army or the diplomatic service.
On leaving school, however, he was such a comfort to his
aunt, and it was so difficult to find a tutor who did not
give him instant dyspepsia, that he was found suddenly too
old to go in for either. His aunt rejoiced; she would have
missed him too much, and he was now permanently free
for the sports, handicaps, drives, and matches of the neighbourhood, whence he could bring home those cups, ciga-
rette-cases, and other rewards of which she was so proud.

She had a verandaed house called "Eglamont," in a
pleasant garden. Eugene had his own rooms and key, his
spirits and tobacco, his fox-terrier and spaniel, a day's hunting when he wished; he shot well, and was welcome with
his gun to the landed neighbours, or on the local yachts,
where he looked to the life in a yachting cap. He had no
patrimony, but his aunt had just enough for two. A self-
effacing woman, she concerned herself entirely with seeing
that Time made no changes in the life of him on whom
she doted. No girls, however much he impressed them,
lean in his very good clothes, detached him from her roof.
It was less dangerous to prefer, platonically at least, the
society of barmaids and married women.

So the years passed by him, embalmed in her affection, in
sport, and cigarettes; till, at the age of twenty-eight, he fell
in love with the wife of a naval commander, with whom
he yachted and played billiards. She was a grey-eyed young
woman, with great good humour, and an admirable figure.
They had leased a house within a stone's throw of "Eglamont" before the naval commander retired to the China

station for two years. Not, indeed, till after his departure was Eugene aware of his feelings. Loyal to one with whom he had played games, he took himself in hand at once, and would sit gloomily pulling his fox-terrier's ears and smoking cigarette after cigarette, sooner than go and see her. In 1890 the phrase "playing the game," had not as yet come in, and he was confined to fortification by the term, "not sporting." The young woman, however, whose name was Mollie, had Venetian-red hair; and he was startled one morning by her appearance with a letter in her hand. She had come to read him a message from her husband. After that it seemed natural that she should often come. The effort of saying "Look here, you know, you mustn't; I'm gone on you," exhausted his defences; nor was it easy to remember a man who, after all, was too old for her, and would not be back for two years. They remained, however, on platonic terms, partly because of their loyalty to the absent commander, and partly because Eugene was not accustomed to any form of energy outside sport.

So he would sit in his long chair, a cigarette between the yellow-stained fingers of one hand, and his fox-terrier's ear between the yellow-stained fingers of the other hand, staring at her and casting out, between his filed-looking teeth, his short laughs and answers to her rallying talk. So it might have gone on for the two years, if her hair, one evening, had not been too much for Plato.

Eugene woke up next morning genuinely shocked—he had not been "sporting." And yet, it was impossible to resist her. For a fortnight the affair proceeded, till one morning she arrived with a telegram in her hand, and on her face an expression remorseful, elated, tearful, glad. The commander had died on a boat expedition up a Chinese river. The news was three weeks old.

"Gene," she said, "isn't it awful, and isn't it—isn't it wonderful in a way! After all, we—we haven't committed—and we can—we can be——" She stopped; his face was copper-coloured. He stammered out: "Poor Bink! Poor old chap!"

She went away dreadfully upset. Next day he had violent dyspepsia.

During the following weeks of seclusion under his aunt's care, he had time to see the matter in all its bearings; it had become evident to him that he was on the edge of being married. It would need inertia almost amounting to effort to avoid that fate. Had he enough? Thinking of her hair, he felt a sinking in that part of him nourished just then solely on Benger's food. In the third week it came to him by inspiration that he knew a "Johnny" about to start on a six weeks' yachting cruise. That evening, eluding his aunt, he made his way to the "Lion's Tail," and over a game of billiards proposed to the "Johnny," and was accepted. That night he was free from pain for the first time.

Leaning over the side in the sun, on his friend's yacht a week later, he felt a kind of regretful deliverance. He wrote from Fowey:

"DEAR MOLLIE—I have been very seedy, but am feeling as right as rain again. This is a nice little hooker. We shall be hanging about in her most of the summer. The weather is jolly, at present. I hope you are fit. It was a shock to me to hear about poor old 'Bink.' Poor old chap! What awful luck! With the best,

"Yours ever,

"GENE."

He did not return to Baymouth till October. He hardly

knew whether to be glad or sorry that she had left. A letter from London informed him that she could not live on her "mouldy pension," and had started a milliner's shop. He admired her pluck, her energy. She sent her love and hoped that his "poor tummy" was stronger. She mentioned theatres—she was evidently having quite a good time. Just one sentence began: "Gene, don't you ever ——" it had been crossed through. He felt that she had "sand."

He settled down to the sports of the season; and time passed like a game that is played.

He was thirty-eight; a little more dried, with a grey hair or two, when she came down to Baymouth again with her second husband, "an old sportsman" of fifty with any amount of "brass," and a "dicky" chest. He was "no end" glad to see her, looking "so jolly fit," with her hair as red as ever. "The old sportsman" played quite a good game of Bridge—just then coming in. They resumed their relations quietly under his nose. She had never stopped loving him all this time, she said. He was touched and flattered, and would sit in his long chair with a cigarette between the yellow-stained fingers of one hand, and the ear of his spaniel between the yellow-stained fingers of the other hand, staring up at her, and emitting his little dry laugh, while she babbled joyously.

The Boer war began—he had thought "those Johnnies" couldn't ride or shoot "for nuts"; he became surprised. It got on his mind a good deal. In December he noticed a great change in Mollie; she grew excitable. And then one day, clinging to him, she said it couldn't go on, they would have to "kick-over"; she couldn't bear that old man any more. Gene must take her away—he must—divorce and all; it wouldn't take a year until they could be married. Extremely copper-coloured, he smoothed her. "Easy-on!" he muttered. "You're off colour, old girl. What's the

matter with the old sportsman? He seems a harmless sort
of old Johnny."

She flung off his hand. Oh! yes; what did he know
—what did he care? He had no blood in him! She was
altogether unjust. He told her not to be a goose. She
clung to him—she called him a "mummy." He said:
"If you don't shut up, I'll spank you!" She raved at him.
Couldn't he see—couldn't he feel—she was only thirty-
three—to be taken away from Gene—to be tied to that
old hog—with his—and his—and his——

He smoothed her again; told her to go "steady over
the stones." They were very well off as they were.

"Yes," she said suddenly, "but he suspects."

"Oh!" he said, and sat down in his long chair. He had
seen, suddenly, an effort before him. He had a pain in his
diaphragm. He lighted a cigarette. His teeth at that moment looked very filed.

The effort before him took shape in the watches of
the second night. Enlist! After all, what would it be?
Only, as it were, a long day's hunting, the exertion of it
nothing compared with that of running away with Mollie
to an ultimate marriage. He had four days' severe dyspepsia
—then took an early train to Exeter, and joined the
Imperial Yeomanry. They wanted fellows of his stamp
who could ride and shoot. His aunt was horrified; it
seemed to her the end of the world. He rallied her. It
would be a "picinic." She admired his patriotism. They
wanted him at once, he said. He left without having again
seen his young and ardent woman. He wrote to her from
Plymouth, on his way out:

"DEAR MOLLIE—I was awfully sorry not to see you
to say good-bye. The Johnnies in my troop ride pretty
well, but they can't shoot for nuts. We're all as keen as
mustard to give these Boer jokers a knock. I hope you'll

have a good winter, and get some hunting. I shall think
of you riding the chestnut. Well—so long, Mollie.

                    "Yours with the best,

                                        "GENE."

He rather enjoyed the campaign, and developed a talent
for stalking. He had drilled three of those "jokers," when
he himself received a bullet through the calf. While in
hospital, he developed enteric, and when convalescent was
discharged and invalided home. Leaner and browner than
ever, he lay in a long chair with a cigarette in his yellow
fingers, staring with his steel-coloured eyes at some con-
versationalist of the female sex, and occasionally emitting
his little high laugh.

"Well, Aunt Susan," he said, on reaching Baymouth.
His aunt shed tears of rapture. He renewed his life as if
it had never been broken. The young woman and her
husband were no longer there. And ten more years passed
like a game that is played.

He was forty-nine when his Aunt Susan died. It upset
him; she was a "good old soul." "That old josser," her
lawyer, worried him awfully about business. She seemed
to have been living on her capital. All he would have
would be the proceeds of the house. It was sold under his
feet. He and his fox-terrier were compelled to move out.
They moved to lodgings close to the "Lion's Tail." He
experienced almost at once the lack of Aunt Susan; he
had to think of money. It was "an awful bore." His
billiards and bridge became systematic. He could no longer
afford to hunt unless a friend mounted him. Still, he got
along—there were few evenings when he did not make
his five to ten shillings over the green baize—large and
small. And five years passed as a game that is played.

He was fifty-four when the Great War broke out. It

roused him as nothing had ever roused him yet. Those
German "jossers" wanted a good hiding. Sitting in his
long chair with a cigarette between the yellow fingers of
one hand and his cocker spaniel's ear between the yellow
fingers of the other, he nerved himself for an effort. Two
or three months passed in the process, then he journeyed
up to London and presented himself at the headquarters of
an Officers' Training Corps. He asked for a commission
on the strength of his service in the Boer war. They were
sorry—they wanted men of his stamp, but he was too old
for a commission. He persisted that he could ride and shoot.
They looked at him, and somebody remarked: "Yes, but can
you think?"

He went very copper-coloured, looked at them deeply,
and left the room. If those "toshers" thought they were
going to win the war by thinking——! He travelled
back to Baymouth, and enrolled himself a Special Constable. It was his duty to guard a culvert. He did it sitting on a shooting-stick, with a cigarette between the yellow fingers of one hand, and the yellow fingers of the
other hand playing with the ears of his cocker spaniel.

Think! He had plenty of time to think, out there, week
in, week out, in various weather. He would listen to the
dripping stillness, or the soughing of the wind in the neigh-
bouring spinney, and wish that one of those "Hun Johnny-
birds" would appear and give him sport. Now and again
he stalked some innocuous person, who came near his culvert; but there was never anything "really doing." In
sheer boredom he took to thinking about how to improve
his income. What little he had could easily be doubled,
he was sure, by any "chap who knew the ropes." He set
himself to know them, by reading newspapers. And three
years passed as a game that is played.

During those years he doubled his income—on paper

—but owing to circumstances that no chap could have foreseen, he was receiving less of it than before he began to increase it. He was literally compelled to seek for a paid job. They gave him something in connection with a hospital. In 1919 the hospital was closed; the war being over, there was nothing for anybody to do, and his income was now just half the insufficient amount it had been before he increased it. In fact, it was about a pound a week; and prices double what they had been. He shot his dog Quiz—"poor old chap"; sold his gun, and changed to a back bedroom in a by-street, where he could sit in what sun there was, and settled down to live on "fags" and billiards. "Bet you a lunch," was his formula, varied by "Bet you fifty cigarettes"—he seldom lost. His clothes were still those he had worn in the days of Aunt Susan, pressed under his heavy leather trunk, and only put on when he went out to the "Lion's Tail" at noon. The mornings he spent in an old blue dressing-gown, smoking cigarette after cigarette, and conning some derelict paper picked up in the bar. He never pitied himself, but he would now and again go copper-coloured, thinking of his income and the newspapers.

On the parade, in the spring of 1921, a lady sat down beside him. He recognised her at once—his old flame, Mollie, and "pretty long in the tooth," too! He made no sign of recognition—hadn't forgotten her calling him a "mummy" last time he had seen her, and that his clothes were not what they had been. But suddenly she turned and said: "Why, it's Gene! So you're still here!" It seemed to him odd. Where else should he be? And how was he? She, herself, hadn't been at Baymouth since. She was a widow again. "Oh! And aren't we old! Why, you're quite white, Gene, and so should I be, if I didn't——"

He grinned. Old Mollie had always been a "sport."

"And to think you nearly 'knocked me out' twice over, Gene!" She looked him slowly up and down. "Poor old Gene, you look rather 'on your uppers'!"

He showed his filed teeth, and said:

"What dammed cheek! You always were a cheeky kid!"

Something came into her eyes—a sort of light.

"You must come and dine with me, Gene. I'm at the Courtfield."

He answered stiffly, "Thanks."

He still had an old dress suit, and one white shirt with cuffs intact. In the next few days he used it several times. She could never elicit from him where he lived. He just grinned, or emitted his high laugh. He began to perceive that she had "tumbled to" his one dress shirt, and pitied him. He did not like it. One evening after dinner, while he was sitting in a long chair with a cigarette in the yellow fingers of one hand and the other hand dangling to the floor, she proposed to him. He grinned, and called her "a little knoop." But next day he was down with a severe attack of dyspepsia. There was something disgusting to him in her wanting at her age to marry him out of pity. If she thought he was "such a tail-down Johnny," she was jolly well mistaken. For a fortnight he stayed in his room, reading old *Pink 'Uns*, and living on Benger's and cigarettes. Only when he had none left did he emerge. To his relief, she was gone.

He had seldom played billiards better than in the week that followed.

Then a real disaster befell him. His hands suddenly began to shake—he couldn't play "for nuts." It meant that he must live on a pound a week. He began to sit stiller than ever, thinking of what he could do. "Bear-

leading some young cub"——something in a riding-school;
he even thought of wheeling a Bath chair, of billiard-
marking, of clerking to a bookmaker. But all such occu-
pations would necesitate his leaving Baymouth, where he
was so well known; and the exertion of such uprooting
was beyond him. Besides, he had no interest anywhere
else, and for such careers interest was necessary. In a
sort of coma, time went by. Ten shillings borrowed here
and there, "tick" with his old landlady——"poor old soul";
the sale of little odd bits of salvage from Aunt Susan's days,
eked out his existence for the next six months. And then
he plunged. A "josser" of his acquaintance who bred
dogs was going out of business. Selling out his one remaining stock of value, he bought it. With the paid
help of a "joker" out of a job, he put up extra kennels.
It was the most definite work he had ever done. In memory of his shot spaniel Quiz——"poor old chap!"——he bred
cockers.

For over a year nearly everything went well——he spent
most of his capital, and had three large litters of pedigree
pups. He passed hours among the "little beggars," a cigarette between his lips, his yellow fingers crumpling their
ears or feeling their points, while their little avid tongues
licked all of him within reach. They were a great pleasure
to him, not the less so for their promise of ten pounds
apiece, and twenty pounds if over distemper. He debated
whether to have them inoculated and sell them with a
guarantee. Nature took the matter out of his hands before
he had made the effort of decision.

The violent distemper of that season came down like
a wolf on his pups, and all but two died. "The poor
little black beggars!" For the first time since he went
to school he almost shed tears. He had sat up with them
night after night, had buried them one after the other.
It was "rotten luck." When the holocaust was over he

was compelled to sell the kennel, lock, stock, and barrel, to pay the bills he had run up. He had fifty pounds left. The efforts of that past year and its final disaster had produced in him a perfect fatalism. For fourteen months he lived on the fifty pounds, his watch, his family seal, the remains of his wardrobe. He never mentioned his condition, and would sit whole afternoons on the high seat in the billiard room of the "Lion's Tail," watching the the game being played, and thinking: "They can't play for nuts." What people thought of him sitting there, lean and white-haired, with his drawn copper-coloured face and thirsting eyes, with his grin, and his well-cut clothes shiny from age, he neither knew nor cared. He had to sit somewhere. And here he got cigarettes, and once in a way a drink was offered him. His friends he had exhausted—he had borrowed from them and was never able to repay; his acquaintances began to shun him for fear that he would borrow. He was "down and out."

One morning his landlady, "poor old soul," came to him crying. She owed money. He couldn't—she supposed—pay her just a little? He called her an "old fussbox," and told her to buck up. That afternoon he put his tooth-brush, shaving brush and razor in the pocket of his old blue overcoat, sold his old bowler and his spare shirt for seven-and-six, bought two hundred fags and a ticket down the coast. The "poor old soul" would be able to let his room, at least. . . .

*   *   *   *   *

In the shelter, huddled into the corner out of the increasing wind, he passed his shaking hand over the bone and skin of his face; then diving it into his pocket, brought out a paper packet. Still ten cigarettes, but he felt too

sick and empty to smoke them. If the sun would come
out, he would get into it and have a sleep. He was "fed
up." Some "jokers" in his place would make for a work-
house, or take a brick and heave it through a window,
get "quodded" and fed. Not much! Easier, more dignified, to sit on, here. If only the sun would come out
and warm him! These "damn-cold" nights his heart was
giving him "beans." He thought, with a grin, of his Aunt
Susan—the "old girl" would have a fit if she could see
him; so would "old Mollie," or his landlady, "poor old
soul!" He shivered, so that his teeth rattled. People would
notice him. He would get under the lee side of a fish-
ing-boat till it was dark. He stood up with difficulty,
and began to move slowly towards the beach and the
huddle of drawn-up boats.

With hands deep-thrust into his pockets, he tried to
look like any other "johnny" crossing that little space.
He sat down exhausted between two boats. An "old
josser" was looking down at him from the parade; he
took up a pebble, and with a shaking hand threw it at a
log of driftwood ten yards or so away. Nobody would
notice a chap throwing pebbles. He threw them at long intervals. His hand shook so that he could not aim—could
not hit "the darned thing." It angered him. Who would
bet him he didn't hit it five times out of fifty? He groped
slowly for the pebbles, amassed a little heap, and counted
fifty. Yes, he would hit "the darned thing" five times
in fifty. He began. He missed his first sixteen shots,
then hit the log twice running, and, taking out a cigarette, he rested. He smoked slowly—he was two pebbles
up.

The sun had come out, and shone full on him over
the edge of the old boat. He turned his face to it; then,
taking up a pebble, began again. His hand shook worse
than ever; he missed eleven times, then "got it plumb

centre." Three hits in thirty shots—just up to his points.
Again he took a cigarette and rested. Two hits to make
in twenty shots—odd if he couldn't win that bet! The
log began to have the qualities of an opponent, to be
endowed with a perverse life of its own. Time was
when he would have hit that "joker" every time! His
cigarette went out. He leaned against the boat, and closed
his eyes. Cold sweat oozed from him; things sank around
him. He rested, half-conscious; came to again, and saw
that log, as if grinning at him, with the sun on it. He
groped up a pebble, and feebly flung it. A hit—by George!
The devil would be in it now if he couldn't make the
other in nineteen shots. On his face, bony and copper-
coloured in the sinking sunlight, a grin was fixed—he
flung and flung. Miss after miss after miss—thirteen
running! "Curse! Couldn't throw for nuts. Get the
damned thing or bust!" Miss after miss after miss. He
had three more pebbles, and he paused.

The setting sun still shone; a seagull with brightened
wings was passing within gunshot. As a boy he remembered he had shot a seagull—before he had learned to be
a sportsman. Three more shots! He was tempted to get
up and lob them. But could he get up? Besides, he must
"play the game" with the darned old log! He had once
claimed a ball "out" at tennis, when he knew that it was
in. It was the sort of thing one didn't like remembering. He raised his arm. Look at it shaking—how could
a fellow throw with an arm like that? The pebble flew
wide. Two more! He remembered a "beak" at his public
school who used to bowl round-arm. Nobody had bowled
round-arm for forty years and more. Give it a chance!
He swung his trembling arm three times in practice, then
took up the last pebble but one. Now for it! His whole
body swung with his arm. Whump! A faint, exultant
whoop came from his lips. A stab went through his breast-

bones—it "hurt like the devil!" He fell back, collapsed under the tarry boat, still as a mummy. . . . And so next day they found him.

circa 1924.

THE GIBBET

I CAN'T describe the street I turned into then—it was like no street I have ever been in, so long, so narrow, so regular, yet somehow so unsubstantial that one had sometimes a feeling that walking at the grey houses on either side one would pass through them. I must have gone miles down it without meeting even the shadow of a human being, when just as it was growing dusk I saw a young man come silently out as I supposed of a door, though none was opened. I can describe neither his dress nor figure. Like the street, he looked unsubstantial, and left on me an impression as of hunger. Yes, the expression on his shadowy face haunted me; it was so like that of a starving man before whom someone has set a meal down, then snatched it away. And now out of every house on either side young men like him started forth in that mysterious manner, all with that hungry look on their almost invisible faces. They seemed to gaze at me as I passed as if they were looking for someone, till, peering at one of them, I said:

"What do you want—whom do you want?"

He gave me no answer, and by now it was so dark that I could not see his face at all—none of their faces, and only had the feeling of being hungrily watched as I went along, it seemed for ever, without getting to any turning out of that interminable street. At last in desperation I doubled in my tracks and began walking back in the direction whence I had come. A lamplighter must have been following me, for now every lamp was lighted, giving a faint glittering greenish glare, as might lumps of phosphorescent matter hung up in the dark. The hungry phantom-like young men had vanished, and I was wondering where they could have gone when I saw—some

131

distance ahead—a sort of greyish whirlpool stretching across the street, under one of those lamps that flickered like a marsh light. A noise was coming from that swirl or whatever it was, for it seemed to be raised above the ground—a ghostly sound, swishing as of feet amongst dry leaves, deepened by the gruntings of some deep sense satisfied. I crept forward till I made out that it was really formed of human figures whirling slowly round and round the lamp in what seemed to be a dance. And suddenly I stood still in horror. Every other figure of those dancers was a skeleton, and between every two skeletons danced a young girl in white, so that the whole swirling ring was formed alternately of skeletons and these grey-white girls. They took no notice of me, and I crept a little nearer still. Yes! these skeletons were the young men I had seen starting out of the houses as I passed, with the look of queer and awful hunger on their faces that now seemed to grin. The girls who danced between them had wan, pitiful beauty, and their eyes were turned to the skeletons whose long hands grasped theirs, as though begging them to return to flesh. Not one noticed me, so deeply were they all absorbed in their mystic dance. Then I saw what they were dancing round. Above their heads, below the greenish lamp, a dark thing was dangling. It swung and turned there like a joint of meat roasting before a fire—the fully dressed body of an elderly man. The green lamplight glinted on his grey hair, and on his bloated features when the face came athwart the light. It swung slowly from left to right, and the dancers as slowly whirled from right to left, always meeting that revolving face, as though to enjoy the sight of it. What did it mean—what were they doing? these sad shapes rustling round the obscene thing suspended there! What strange and awful rite was I watching by the ghostly phosphorescence of that lamp? If those hungry skeletons and wan-grey girls haunted and amazed me, much more haunting and gruesome was that dead face up there with the impress still on it of bloated life; how it gripped and horrified me, with its dead fishy eyes and its neck thick-rolled with flabby flesh, turning and turning on its invisible spit to the sound of feet swishing in dead leaves, and those grunting sighs. What was this ghostly revenge on the gibbeted figure which yet had a look of cold and fattened power? Who was it they had caught and swung up there, like some dead crow, to sway in the winds of heaven? What awful crime towards these skeleton dancers and pale maidens could this elderly man be expiating?

And I remembered with a shudder how those young men had looked at me as I passed, and suddenly it came to me: I was watching the execution of MY generation. There it swung, gibbeted by the youths and maidens whom, through its evil courses, it had murdered. And seized with panic I ran forward up the street staight through the fabric of my dream, that swayed and rustled to left and right of me.

1914–1918.

'The breeze would have savèd him, you know,' said the mate.

Out of a cloudless sky,
Into a sapphire sea,
To the tune of a windless sigh,
That is drawn in the tops'ls three,
The sun sinks fast thro' a burning haze
To the heart of a sapphire sea.

Over the shadowed deep,
Topped with an oily swell,
To the hours of the night asleep
In the chime of her muffled bell
The spent ship prays—and her spirit fails
On the heave of the sullen swell.

   *   *   *   *   *

Fanning the crimson flare
Lit by the coming dawn,
Thro' the hush in the breathless air
Of the night that is past and gone,
The wind speeds swift to the weary sails,
In a song of the coming morn.

But away from the stifled ship,
Fleeter than any wind,
With a kiss on the twisted lip
Of the face that she leaves behind,
A breath steals forth—and the wind but plays
On a mask without stir or mind.

SIX bells clanged the dawning of the last hour in the
midnight watch. I dropped my cards, for it was the
peculiar custom to stop whist just as the bell sounded.

"Time up!" said the Captain regretfully, mopping his
brow. "How do we stand, Jenny?"

His wife's voice—"Eight and three eleven, and four———"
rose in a vinegary triumph of addition from across the
saloon table, to culminate in an emphatic "Fifteen points."

"Good! I rather think that's the best night yet, sir. Bed,
Jenny. Good night, gentlemen. A hot night, ain't it?"

"Good night, Captain! Good night, Mrs. Cape! Coming on deck, Jacques?"

"No," said my partner; "bed for this child, g'night";
and murmuring a disgusted "Fifteen points—and the
vinegar—and the heat—phew!" he shut his cabin door
with a jerk.

I climbed the stern hatchway, and joined the three men
lounging against the skylight on the poop. The moon hung
hazily between the softly flapping sails of the idling ship.
Out of the deadly calm waters a little purposeless heave
rocked her ever and anon to this side and that, and the old
shellback at the useless wheel whistled softly to himself,
as he looked vainly for the ship's wake in the oily tropical
ocean.

The Southern Cross dipped afar on the port quarter, and
innumerable stars spangled the stilly depths of the dark
heavens. The curiously dissonant miaul of the fo'c'sle cat
hit the ear, through the sultry stifling air, with a sense of
the relieved ridiculous.

"Dosé fallows, you know" (he pronounced it "gnau"),
said the mate in his slightly nasal, foreign accent, evidently
resuming, "it's very curious you know, day rraally haven't
any feelings."

"Do you mean, they feel no emotions, as we understand
the word?" said young Raymond impatiently, his intoler-
ance of human beings so constituted ringing in the high-
pitched tones of his clear voice.

"Not a blessed one!" said a third voice from the ship's
side, shrill and worn. "Yellow devils! Yellow devils!
They've only one virtue."

"And that, Doctor?"

"Opium, sirree. They're tolerable when they're opium-drunk."

The mate looked up sharply, and with his brown, almond-shaped Slav eyes scrutinised keenly the dim figure of the speaker; and his mouth, between the close-trimmed, pointed beard and drooping moustaches, took a more than usually cynical and mournful curve.

"You are severe, Doctor," he said; but the other, without answering, turned away, and leaned over the bulwark wearily.

"Ah! that is bad, you know," I heard the mate say to himself under his breath.

"Yes," said the shrill voice presently from the darkness, "you may have seen 'em, and you may talk about 'em, but you don't *know* them. You've not worked in China Town amongst John Chinaman, as I've worked. I guess you've not seen 'em born, and die, and marry, as I've seen 'em. Ugh! devils—devils—hog-skinned, slit-eyed devils!"

"It is all tempèrrament, you know," said the mate, "dosé fallows, you know, they are different all through, it is not a question of degree. A white man will never understand how their minds worrk. Will you have a cigarette, Doctor?" He watched the thin face and trembling hand closely, and shook his head, as the Doctor turned back with his lighted cigarette to the ship's side.

"It is bad, you know," he muttered again to himself. Young Raymond had strolled to the wheel, and was standing talking cheerily to the helmsman; the heat seemed to have no effect on his buoyant spirits. I, stretched on a locker, fanned myself lazily with the mate's cap, and the mate himself sat in his favourite attitude with his hands clasping his knees, his chin sunk on his chest. Presently the Doctor began to talk again, more to himself than to us.

"What a night!" he said. "What a ghastly, hellish,

stifling night! Look at that oily pond, can't you feel the heat lifting out of it into your face? I used to think nothing could lick the Queensland bush, but Great Lordy! this is worse, many points worse; there was always a kind of a breeze there and some stir of life, but this flat, oily waste—Oh! for a breath of air. I can't breathe; I tell you, Armand, I can't breathe!" He turned round to the mate fiercely, and threw out his thin hands, as if to thrust from him some suffocating weight. "What's the good of you sea-men," he laughed a feeble hoarse laugh, "if you can't fetch some sort of air up out of your hell-doomed oceans?"

"No fear, Doctor, we'll get you some before long annyway; three days flat calm is a big spell even for the Doldrums. How's her head, mv son?" he called out to the grey-bearded helmsman.

"Nor-nor West, zurr."

"Is she doing anny?"

"Noa, zurr, but zims there's a but of a swell tu th' Sou East, mebbe we'll 'ave wind before the marnin'." The shellback spat on his hand and held it out, then shook his head doubtfully.

"The dawn will bring it," said the mate, "you will see."

"Not to me," said the Doctor to himself, "I'm through."

Young Raymond turned at the sound of the dreary despairing voice.

"What's that?" he said. "Through! we're *all* through, we're all kippered to the nines; don't be so beastly egotistical, Doctor, you've got no blooming monopoly." The sunny ring of his voice through the jaded night was as refreshing as a breeze, but the Doctor only said moodily:

"Yes, my friend, but I guess you weren't fried to start with, there was still some English juice in you; you haven't been spread-eagled on a gridiron for seven years till everything's been sucked out of you, even sleep."

"Sleep!" echoed the Doctor shrilly, and his thin scarecrow of a figure writhed against the railing of the bulwark, "I haven't slept for *weeks*—I'm going home, *home*, I tell you, after seven God-forsaken years, but I'd give it all, and chuck in the rest of my life, for twenty-four hours of natural sleep." At the word "natural" the mate shifted uneasily in his seat, and his foot beat a tattoo incessantly on the deck.

"There will be trouble," he said softly, "big trouble, unless we get the wind, you know. Come, my dear fallow," he went on to the Doctor, "what is the matter with you to-night, you were not even amusèd with the Wray baby—oh!" he laughed with a sudden unrestrained merriment curious to listen to in that sultry, joyless air, "that is an interesting little animal. Did you see Cotter fill it with plum-duff at dinner, and Mrs. Wray opposite laughing all the time, you know, and little Wray looking 'orrified—ah-ha! and the little animal likèd it, you know," his laughter died out as suddenly and he gazed at the Doctor with his mournful eyes—the eyes of a man who has been to the edge of the world many times, and looking over—come back again.

"You are hipped to-night, you are quite dull, you know. Tell us a yarn of John Chinaman; he has a most curious individuality, annyway."

There was silence a moment, then the spanker boom creaked slightly from pure inaction, as floors creak in houses at the dead of night, and a spark from the mate's cigarette floated straight upwards in the dead air; then came a weird, droning sing-song whisper from the bulwarks.

"Once upon a time," it said, "there was a poor devil of a doctor whose lot it became, after many wanderings, to minister for his living, in an oven, to the extremities of John Chinaman, whereby he learnt many things—for instance, that it was good to eat puppy-dog and go unshaven, that there was no such thing as right or wrong, beauty or ugliness, cleanliness or dirt, heaven or hell—that there was no end to the miseries of the white man, and neither end nor beginning to the miseries of the yellow man. But also" —the whisper almost died away, "he learnt one supreme good, νο καλδν that without which man withers—life has no taste, no colour, no scent—the great, the glorious—my, God! O my God!" The voice from the faintest whisper, rose suddenly to a scream. With a spring young Raymond's lithe white-clothed figure was by the Doctor's side, his arm round his neck.

"Steady, dear old boy!" he said.

The meaning of those muttered sayings had suddenly been rendered plain, and the mate stood leaning forward with his long arms half stretched out towards the Doctor. The melancholy fatalism of his face, that outcome of his Slav blood, was veiled by a look of sorrowful concern.

"Ohé!" he said, "Ohé! tck, tck——"

As for me, I moved swiftly to the wheel, and stood between the group of men and the helmsman, speaking to him at random, in the instinctive dread of what was coming next on the shrill tones that lifted themselves behind me.

"Yes," said the worn voice, "look at me!—look at me! —what am I? What have I sunk to? I who was even as you—public school!—'Varsity—Bart's—what's the use of it all? Look at me, I say, look"—he clutched with one hand at the arm thrown about him; and as if answering the hysterical cry, the moonlight streamed from behind the main tops'le, with a cruel suddenness, full on to the two men. It lit up the bright, fresh face and yellow hair of the one, tall and lithe and radiantly white—and threw into a ghastly relief the other, long, shrunken and shambling, with his twisted yellow face and sunken hunted eyes, with the little brown streak at the corner of the thin distorted mouth, the lank discoloured hair, the writhing skeleton hands. He cowered as the light fell upon him, and buried his head like a child on young Raymond's shoulder.

When I turned again, old Carey, the shellback, was looking steadily at the deck, and, contrary to all orders, spitting vigorously upon it.

"Fact is, we'm tu fur tu the east; you see, zurr, these y'er ca'ms is all along o' that."

What answer I made to the soft west-country drawl I know not, because it is bewildering to hear a man's sobs drawn under hard pressure against a linen coat. Then the mate was speaking.

"Come down to your bunk, my dear fallow, it will be all right, you know; I will give you some things to make you sleep."

"Sleep!" came out of the sobs, as a voice might come out of a grave, on to which the earth was being shovelled. "My God! if I could sleep *without* . . . Armand, for pity's sake make me sleep——"

"There! there!" young Raymond spoke as to a child.

As swiftly as it had streamed forth, the moonlight hid itself behind a kindly sail, and the three soft footsteps, moving along the deck, slowly died away out of my hearing.

"Might yu 'appen to 'ave zum baccy, zurr? The mate's gone down, yu zee, an' it du be rale 'ot to-night, that's zartin." I gave the understanding Carey out of my pouch, and we smoked in a sympathetic silence.

*   *   *   *   *

I woke with a start; a faint light was showing through the open port-hole, and the half-drawn curtain of the bunk wavered unsteadily.

"She's moving," I thought, feeling with a vast sense of relief the fluttering pulse beginning to beat at last in the wind-logged ship.

"Yes, there's a breeze from the south-east; get up!"
Young Raymond was standing by the side of the bunk, his
white clothes unchanged, but with a face unknown to me,
so grave, drawn, and sunless was it.

"What's wrong?"

"The Doctor!" he said. "Come!"

We crossed the dark saloon, unswept and ungarnished,
just as it had been left the evening before. Raymond
silently drew aside the green baize curtain of a cabin on the
starboard side. Within it stood the mate, stooping over a
figure stretched limply on the lower bunk; he looked up as
we came in, and withdrew his hand, with something in it,
from under the pillow.

"Look!" he said, holding up a little inlaid box. "I was
afrayd of it; I lookèd for it last night, you know——"
there was a curious note of appeal in his voice—"but dosé
fallows are so cunning, you know."

I looked at the face lying upturned to the growing light.
It was no longer twisted; the eyes stared quietly at the
roof of the bunk, the hands were crossed peacefully on the
sunken chest. In that face, which had writhed the night
before in hunted agony, there remained only the little
brown stain at the corner of the mouth to mark it as the
same.

"Dead?"

"Quite." The mate knelt, and reverently drew the lids
over the quiet eyes.

Young Raymond was leaning silently apart against the
side of the cabin, his head framed in the open port-hole,
and his face was very grey and drawn. I turned from him
to the mate.

"How?"

He answered the double question of my glances hurriedly.

"No, it was an accident, see——" he unscrewed the lid of

the little box, and counted the tiny black-brown pills in it. "Six—seven—ayt—there were manny happy hours, you see; while desé were here, he would not have done it, you know. No, it was an accident—perrhaps he took one too manny, and that"—he laid his hand gently over the dead man's heart. "Poor fallow! I likèd him greatly."

There was a long silence in the little cabin; the faint "lip-lip" of the rising waves against the ship's side seemed very far away somehow, and the measured tramp of the second mate on the poop above sounded in muffled harmony to our thoughts—then six bells rang out clear and full.

"It is Cotter's watch still," said the mate, "I am free for an hour yet. We must talk, you know."

He moved over and shut the door, then seated himself on the side of the dead man's bunk with a reverent callousness born of an intimate familiarity with many kinds of death.

The ends of the Doctor's dusky crimson sash hanging over the upper bunk quivered slightly, with the faint rolling of the ship, against the mate's smoothly dark head, as he crouched forward with his back hunched, and his bearded chin thrust out. His hands were clasped round one knee, the thin leg below them working incessantly with a quick, nervous movement. All the time he was speaking, he looked straight at young Raymond with his mournful eyes, and the latter, who had never moved from his leaning attitude against the cabin side, gazed abstractedly in front of him from out of a growing halo of flame-coloured light. The ship's cat purring softly was rubbing itself slowly against the white trousered leg.

"Dis thing had to happen, you know," said the mate at last. "It was written, you see, there"—he raised a hand and pointed to the still face. "I knew it a long time. I think I knew it when he first came on board at Adelayde; he walkéd down the quay, you know, with that fatiguéd

walk he had, poor fallow, and it was written in his eyes—
they were quite hunted, you know. *I've* rraally been the
doctor on the old galley this journey, you know; he wasn't
fit for it. Hang it all, I have been dosing the shellbacks,
you know, poor devils—ah-ha!" he laughed that sudden
spontaneous laugh that must have come from his lips even
in death, if an idea had commended itself to his sardonic
humour.

"The skipper should never have taken him on board, you
know; but the old fallow was in a hole, he had to get off,
and he had to have a doctor. The old galley is an invalid
ship, you know, and so she has to have a doctor and a cow
—that blessed cow hasn't given anny milk, still she has four
legs, you know—and *I* am the doctor." He gnawed at his
moustache and muttered some words under his breath.

Then young Raymond spoke for the first time.

"Did you know that?" he said, pointing with a shrinking
gesture to the opium box in the mate's hand.

"After Cape Town, I knew it. Guessed it when he came
on board, you know, and shut himself into his cabin for
two days. I got in once, and then I saw what the trouble
was, you know. I lookéd for that"—he held up the box—
"but dosé fallows are so cunning. *He* knew it too, he
knew he was going to hand in his checks, you know. He
uséd to talk to me, and he often said, '*if* I get home.'"
The mate paused. "Well! that is all over, it had to happen,
you know." His voice and face and the resigned dejection
of his whole figure embodied the word "Kismet"; the
threads of the situation, for the moment, had slipped
through his fingers. He sat quite quiet, staring mournfully
in front of him, but the leg beneath his clasped hands never
ceased a second in its nervous movement.

The tramp above, and the "lip-lip" of the little green
waves against the ship's side, were again the only sounds
that broke in on the early silence.

"For the sake of his people," said young Raymond suddenly, taking the little box from the mate's hand.

"Yes, he had an ayged father, you know, a parson in Yorkshire, he was going home to him—after seven years—that is harrd, you know," said the mate dreamily.

"Well?" said Raymond impatiently, and he put the hand that held the box through the open port-hole.

"No—no—look here," said the mate, holding out his hand for the box, "I must tell the skipper, you know," and he put the box away in his pocket. "But you will see, it will be all right, he will leave the whole racket in my hands; he hates a fuss, you know, that old fallow. Besides, it wasn't rraally the opium at the end, you know, it was the heat—his heart was so weakened, you see." He got up and looked earnestly, with narrowed eyes, at the dead man's wasted figure.

"Yes," he said at last, "it was a little joke, the breeze would have savèd him, you know . . . but it will be all right—failure of the haart from the heat . . . and then we shall put him over the side; annyway there will be no post-mortem. Nobody will come in here, you see, except the skipper, and the box will be in my pocket—the wind will take away the smell in time." There was a faint, sweet, sickly smell as of drugs in the close air of the confined space.

"So be it!" said young Raymond, moving from his station against the cabin wall.

"Let us put him to rest, though; his face haunts me, even when I don't look at it," and he shuddered; "the light is too cruel." Keeping his head averted, he took a handkerchief from a drawer, and covered the dead man's face. The flaming East was sending a shaft of orange light through the open port-hole, full upon it, and the effect was not pretty.

"When did he go?" I said, breaking the silence that followed.

"I don't know," said the mate, "but it could not have been long before the breeze came, annyway—he was hardly cold, you know."

Young Raymond faced round to the light with strained eyes.

"I know," he said suddenly, "*I* know, I saw him go, I saw it all. I shall never get it out of my head—never! never!" The mate looked at him half cynically, half concernedly.

"Hang it all, my dear fallow," he said, "death is not an aymiable joker, when you are not used to him, you know; but you mustn't let him play with your narves."

"Nerves?" said young Raymond hoarsely, "you shall tell me if it *is* nerves, Armand, for, by George! I should like to know.

"Well?" said the mate; he had seated himself again in his favourite attitude.

The world seemed suddenly enclosed within the walls of this wooden crib, time was annihilated, everything stood still, there was no longer anything outside—just the cabin —we three—and the dead man. I felt giddy and stifled, but the moment young Raymond began to speak, all that feeling merged in wonder at the intense earnestness in his face and the tones of his voice.

"After we left *him* last night," he said, "I slung my hammock on the main deck, starboard side, just where the gymnastic bars are rigged by the main mast; it seemed cooler there than on the poop. Cotter came out on watch just after I turned in, so it was about midnight, I suppose. I couldn't get the idea of *him* out of my head"; he avoided looking at the dead man always, and stared straight in front of him.

"I could see him tossing and twisting in that bunk, and I couldn't get to sleep for ages; I suppose I must have dropped off at last, though, because I didn't hear two bells go. I woke suddenly out of an awfully jolly dream about home and my people. The moon was down, but it wasn't very dark; there was just that light that comes before the dawn, you know. Oh! yes, I could see all right; I could see pretty clearly right to the starboard hatchway leading up to the poop——that was just facing me as my hammock was slung. It was frightfully hot, suffocating——there wasn't a breath of air——not a breath. I lay awake a few minutes, and then I suppose I dozed off again; but though my eyes were shut, I seemed to have the feeling that something was coming towards me. It grew upon me, so that I must have half raised myself in my hammock, because when I woke again I was sitting up. There was something ——a figure; it came from under the starboard hatch out of the saloon. I could hardly see it in that horrible, misty, unreal light, but it came slowly along the deck close to the bulwark without making any noise. I don't know why I was in a ghastly funk, but it seemed somehow uncanny—— I wasn't properly awake, you see. I waited for it——it seemed hours coming. When it was almost within touch, I saw what——it was——it was——*him*. His head was bent back, and his hands thrown up; he was like a shot bird that's towering for air, you know, but there was no sound, no choke or gasp——I listened for it, but there was none, not even a sigh!"——he paused. "There ought, there must have been a gasp, if it was he," he muttered to himself; "he couldn't have stood like that without a sound. Oh! Armand, the face!"

He spoke in short broken sentences, and his hands twisted here and there in the full agony of recollection.

"The eyes were staring open, as they were before you

—and nothing moved in it—it was a dead face . . . and then it went away again, you know—I don't know *how* it went. I shall never get that look out of my head—never." He drew his hands across his eyes.

"It was far worse than *that* dead face," he said solemnly, pointing to the bunk; "it was the dead face of a *living* man."

"Then?" said the mate.

"Then I lay back in my hammock, not more than a minute, I think—and then I got out and came here, and as I crossed the deck the first of the breeze crossed it too— too late!—he died for want of air, I know he did—just too late, you see!"

"Too late!" echoed the mate softly, nodding his head. "*That* is the joke."

"He was lying here as you found him. I didn't touch him before I came and told you. And, look here! Armand, what have I seen? It scared me."

An infinite and sombre gentleness was in the look the mate bent to meet the trouble in the young face turned to him, but he only said, "That is most interesting. You are not to be pitied, you know, you are to be envied; a man does not often see these things, you know."

"But *what* did I see? *What?* I tell you it scared me."

"I *think*," said the mate slowly—"I don't know, of course—but I think you have seen what very few people have seen. I think there is a time, you know, which comes between life and death. It is perhaps the twilight of the body, you know, and the dawning of the soul—it is that breathless space which these old crafts of our bodies have to go through, you know, where there is no life, and not yet death—the Doldrums of our individualities hanging in the wind." There was a long silence.

"Thanks," said young Raymond at last, and the old

sunny look seemed to creep back into his face through the haunting shadow of fear cast there by the thing he had seen.

"Thanks, old fellow! The dawning of the soul! I like that." He had caught, like a child, at the one idea in the mate's words which appealed to his narrow, sanguine optimism; and only *I* saw the look of wearily gentle cynicism in the mate's face, and heard his words as he turned away out of the cabin, "Yes? If there is such a thing, you know."

So I turned away too from the "valley of the shadow," but young Raymond knelt softly by the bunk and drew the handkerchief from the dead man's face. He could bear to look on him now. The breeze stole in and stirred the hair on the two heads close together.

The words came to me at the door.

"You're all right now, old fellow, aren't you? You've gone home." Then through a choke in the voice, "But oh! my God! your luck was hard!"

1895–1896.

MEMORABLE MOMENTS

I

"WHEN that I was and a tiny little boy—with a hey
and a ho and a hey nonny no!" certain days were
memorable. These were days when my Father's house was
full of preparations for a dinner party, and I would be
hard at work during all the hours not given up to lessons.
First I had to attend the head gardener in the hot-house
and the vinery, selecting the pineapples and grapes, or from
the south wall picking the peaches and nectarines; nor
could I on any account be absent when Henry, the butler,
with two wicker baskets, and my Father opened the cellar
door which kept in that half-nice funny smell, as of gas
and mushrooms. With my hands in my waist-belt and my
legs apart, I would stare up at my Father handling the bottles with extreme care, and with his thin, taper-nailed
fingers holding them up to the light. And I used to pretend
that I was in a dungeon, and be very careful to be in front
when we brought the bottles up.

I had also constantly to be in the kitchen, to see exactly
what was going to be eaten, and be told: "Now, Master
Johnny, don't touch!" I found it advisable, too, to watch
the special polishing which George the groom would give
his buttons, in order that he might take charge of—I forget
exactly what.

All this would be in the morning. The afternoon would
be even more exciting; for, quite early, my friend, Mr.
Sawdy, the greengrocer, who had whiskers and such a pale,
nice face, and was pleased with my society, and my friend
Glover who could wink, would arrive, beautifully dressed,
with white gloves in their pockets (because I saw them),
to help Henry and François put the extra leaves in the din-
ing-table, and lay it and the sideboard. Every time I came

in to see, the room would look more and more snowy and shining, and smell nicer and nicer of melon and pineapple and flowers; till at last I would say to Mr. Sawdy: "I might have a wafer now, Mr. Sawdy." And Mr. Sawdy would look round, and hook one out of the box for me, and shake the box a little so that no one could see there was one gone. And I would eat the wafer—nibbling it ever so slowly from one of its corners upwards—they were lovely wafers, and tasted of something in between.

I was not so interested in the flowers which my Mother would be arranging in the library, and bringing in. I liked the smell indeed, and the colours, but I felt that they were not serious like the melons or the peaches, or the wafers. Nor was I interested in the drawing-rooms on these days, because there was nothing there that was going to be eaten; they just looked all shiny and had no one in them. Sometimes all the twenty-four people, except my Father and Mother, would be coming specially—some all the way from London—in their carriages; but sometimes there would be guests staying in the house, especially my Uncle Wally and my Cousin Evie.

On such occasions I would go and see my Cousin Evie —she was very old, more than twenty—have her hair done by Adèle. It was nice and almost yellow, and was rolled up on a sort of cushion, very high; I would stand at the corner of her dressing-table and turn over the silver things and read the monograms out loud, and smell the powder, and look at her neck and think what a lot of neck it was.

Presently she would say: "Now, Johnny, trot along!" And I would go and sit on the stairs, waiting for my Uncle Wally, because I had to see his waistcoat buttons. He had a very large waistcoat, much larger than my Father's, and more white and shiny; and it took up a lot of room on him because he was not tall, only very broad and square; but he smelled lovely and had three more rings than my Father, because my Father had none; and his face was pale and broad, and had twisty little grey moustaches, and a little grey tuft on his chin; his eyes were pale and blue and round—and they pouted at you; and his collar was very high and shiny and had sharp points, very wide apart, and his chin fitted beautifully between them; and when he walked it was like one of our pigeons.

He seemed to me a very distinguished man. He played billiards beautifully. I always had to see his waistcoat buttons, because of their being black and white with diamonds in the middle. He had a funny broad ribbon, too, coming out of his waistcoat pocket, and some shiny things at the end of it, dangling. He used to tap my chest and tell me to puff it out like a man; but it took me too much time to remember. He used to show me his watch, too; it was yellower and fatter and smoother than my Father's, but it could not strike.

I liked my Uncle Wally best when he sat on the terrace and drank claret cup, because he let me taste it. I had to watch his lips, too, when they made rings of cigar smoke, all blue. He made better rings than my Father, and his voice was interesting to listen to—it had a sort of fat sound.

When I had seen his buttons, I had to go and hear my Father say to my Mother: "Now, Blanche, you'll be late." My Mother would be beautiful with ear-rings and a curl coming down each side of her neck—they were called ringlets. I always wanted to pull them so as to see them curl up again like my toy snake, only I was not allowed. But I might stand in the doorway so that my Father could not go out without wrestling with me; this he would do very seriously, puffing a little to show me how strong I was, then suddenly slide me between his legs and leave me on the floor.

Then my Mother would push my hair up and say: "Now,

Johnny darling, go along to bed," and I would go by one door and come back by another, before Mademoiselle or Nurse could see me, so as to sit at the top of the stairs and look down into the hall.

I could hear the carriages driving up, and see Henry walking across the hall with a lady and gentleman behind him, and hear him say: "General and Mrs. Grim," and then he would stand still at the drawing-room door while they all came up, and blew in his ear, one after the other; and he would say—like this: "Mr. and Lady Evelyn Tushby"; "Sir Edgar and Lady Dulane, and Miss Dulane —ahem!" "Mr. and Mrs. Tureen"; "Mr. and Mrs. Tipping—ahem! ahem!" This lasted a long time, and there was ever such a loud nice noise of talking, which made me feel buzzy and excited. Then Henry shut the door, and it was quiet.

I knew then they had all come, and that was somehow nice. I could see Henry standing all alone down there, and once I saw him put his thumb up to his nose and spread out his fingers and point them at the door. I was very interested. But before I could say, "Henry!" and ask him why, he opened the dining-room door and went in. He always came out again very quickly, and opened the drawing-room door and said: "Dinner is served."

Then I would stand up and put my head over the banisters, because I had to see everybody properly. It was like the Noah's Ark, only the gentlemen were black and shiny white in front, and the ladies had ever so much more skin than Mrs. Noah, and were wider below; and last of all came my Mother and Sir Edgar Dulane, because he was the tallest of all; and my Uncle Wally was the shortest— only he looked very important, he was so broad, and had the largest waistcoat. And just then Mademoiselle used to say: "Jean, *comme tu es méchant; viens donc!*" and that was all, because I never heard and never saw any more.

II

WHEN I was eight years old the world began again for one who, till then, had known nothing of the more glorious flowers in human form—pirates, slavers, smugglers, poachers, brigands, Saracens, Frenchmen, together with those noble British whose pleasure and duty it was to fight against them, year in, year out. I had just had the measles, a disease which expands the soul, and while my spirit was opening, there came to our house the new governess. How old she was I know not—very old, perhaps twenty, but still beautiful. She had broad cheekbones, bright grey eyes, bright brown hair, tight dresses, a nice scent, a romantic turn of mind, and ruled over those books of adventure which it was her first duty to read aloud to us, so that we might listen, sucking tangerine oranges, and get well.

That was the beginning of the new world, wherein every tree was a ship in full sail, to whose top-yards one must ever be climbing; every wardrobe and cupboard the bastion of a castle, or a cliff from which one must leap down; every window made so that one might escape from prison (having refused to give parole); every daisy flower and 'soldier' on the lawns meant to be plucked, and named Sir Lancelot, Sir Lamoracke (oh! memorable sound!), Sir Tristan, Sir Palamedes—and struck against each other until one, or both, of their heads came off, so that one knew —or not—which was the better knight. When all life became a dream of the taking of Arab dhows, of British seamen fighting with sharks, on open rafts, of cutlasses and jungles, of tournaments, and the storming of castles, and the barring out of schoolmasters, with other delights. When stones and beans and marbles in great numbers, manœuvred upon tables, represented Austrians, Italians, Spaniards, Swedes and what not, while one told oneself a delicious

never-ending history of how they killed each other. When
soldiers of lead, set up in somewhat close formation, were
mown down while performing feats of gallantry, by dried
peas from little tin cannons, whose little wires one pulled.
When our tabby kitten was named Puck Hotspur Wilfrid
Cœur-de-Chat Front-de-Bœuf Fitz-Urse; and to dress up
in chain armour (of knitted wool) was the greatest joy in
life. When Time did not exist nor weather, nor any person except in so far as they could be attacked and routed
with great slaughter, or captured and placed somewhere in
the dark. When one never moved without charging, except to climb trees, with a cutlass in one's teeth; and all the
time loved everyone and everything, and only hurt anything by frequent accident.

That was a year bathed in the glamour of imaginary
fighting, and—love for the new governess. The summer
holidays were dim without her; the day of her return—
brilliant August—was one long wandering up the stairs,
and one ecstatic jumping down them; one continual rush
to assure everyone that she was coming, one wide surprise
that they were not so excited as they should have been. And
then a lurking in the cool hall, and a listening for wheels.
They came, rolling, crunching; stopped, and there she
stood, in sunshine! A dash from cover of the darkened
hall; a leap, so that arms were round her neck and legs
round her waist, and all four knotted up together the other
side of her. And a hug so furious that something creaked,
and she gasped out: "Oh! my darling!" Those, too, were
memorable days—of War and Love.

III

THERE is a nook in the county of Devon favourable to
the old pagan spirits of Rock, Wind, Wood, and Water.
On the hillside to the South-West, one of those spirits has

rested so long that he has become incarnate there—a Stone
Man upreared, gigantic, gazing for ever towards the setting
of the sun. To South-East lie out two huge lions of gran-
ite; and over the hill, hounds in full cry after some prey
of a million years ago were caught by the elements and
confirmed in rock. For the elements have strength here.
The wind comes charged with the force of three thousand
miles of sea, travels the highlands of the full moor, gath-
ering scent of peat and heather, and whirls a passion of rain
over the tors and combes. There is no level ground, not a
yard, not an inch, nothing but hill, moor, trees, and far
away, a passionate loveliness of the pink South Devon
'ploughs' and a gleam of sea.

May, when the old apple trees are in bloom, the hedges
creamed with hawthorn flower, the oaks still golden, the
ashes as yet thin-leaved, and every tree of a different
colour; May—when the sky behind that group of brown-
limbed pines is of infinite deep blue edged by flashing cloud;
when from dawn till after day is down cuckoos sing and
pass over in arrowy flight out to the stones of the moor and
the thorn trees that have lived for ever; May—when the
lambs, foals, and young of the red cattle, and every bird
and flower seem full of wonder that they should ever have
been born—May is the grandest month. May, and late
October, when each hillside is coppered with flames of
bracken; the birches thinned and goldened, and the sky
high, and of amethystine blue.

Here the wind drops almost every sunset, as though to let
the evening star come out in peace; the wood-smoke rises
thin and blue, the two brown owls float over the front field
into the low beech-trees—more silent than two brown
dropping leaves. The moonless nights have a star for every
dew-drop spied on the lawn in the mornings. But the
mooned nights bring the greater beauty, for the valley trees
stand knee-deep in mist white as cotton-wool, and the yew-

trees lay long shadows on the wan grass, and a brightness
as of white unearthly birds is gathered beyond the hollies.

I have seen the moon come and hide behind the great
lime-tree, as though she were a Presence, a bright angel
that would just see if all were well.

circa 1920.

NOTES ON FELLOW-WRITERS
PAST AND PRESENT

TRIBUTES TO CONRAD

(SPOKEN AT WARSAW AND CRACOW)

FOR thirty years my best and dearest friend in the writing world was your great fellow-countryman, Joseph Conrad Korzeniovski, one who, as you know, loved England well enough to live there, and become a British subject; and one who in his writing brought new blood and life into English Literature. Though he loved England, his love for his native Poland was very great; I have heard him many and many a time talking of it and of his kin over here. I met him first when he was still a sailor, before he had adopted the profession of letters, thirty-three years ago, and I do not remember that in the thirty-one years of our friendship we ever had the smallest difference.

To my mind, travelling over all those years, the early days come back most vividly; when with the earnestness of comparative youth we discussed all things in heaven and earth and some that seemed beyond those spheres; when Conrad was a writer already acclaimed by connoisseurs (as indeed he was from the very first), but struggling to make good in a world which in those days received unfamiliar genius very grudgingly; and I—I was unknown, a prentice writer trying to find his feet in the deep waters of expression. And I remember that even in those midnight discussions, how thickly pictures, facts, reminiscences, tales of his own adventures, impressions of the men and women he had met, starred his talk, so that we never became fogged in the gloom of the abstract and metaphysical, never lost touch with the tides of human nature. It was the great quality of Conrad that with all his sense of the cosmic, of the enveloping mystery of Nature, he kept ever to the touchstone of fact, never became theoretical and misty, never lost grip of human feeling.

For one of his books he took for motto the dwarf's saying (from Grimm): "Something human is dearer to me than the wealth of all the world." For another he took the motto from Novalis: "It is certain my conviction gains infinitely, the moment another soul will believe in it." For yet another: *"Celui qui n'a connu que des hommes polis et raisonnables, on ne connaît pas l'homme, ou ne le connaît qu'à demi."*

To him nothing that was human was foreign. Through all his work runs this prepossession with the warm human glow of actual life, and with the strange ironies, heroisms, and failings of human nature; it was one of the secrets of the hold he ultimately gained on our affections in England. For we in England are not a theoretical people. Our philosophy is very much a day-to-day concern—we hold by fact. And if there are qualities that we prize beyond others, they are the courage which meets Life as it runs, the common sense which accepts what is and tries to make the best of it, and loyalty to common tasks and ties. These are very much the qualities which, clothed in the magic of his special phrasings and his poet's moods, form the very soul of Conrad's work, and were the virtues which adorned his life. So you see he was never a stranger to our spirits over there. Those practical men who form the bulk of our island population were spiritually at anchor when they read his tales. He was a writer with whom they felt they could put to sea and trust to stand by them. And that is more than one can say of many a writer whose blood is English.

Partly because he was writing in a language not native to him, marvellously though he used it, he was sometimes too intricate and subtle for the English reader; sometimes, owing to his Slavonic blood, too brooding and conscious of Fate; but at bottom he and we believed in the same virtues of sober courage and positive loyalty, and we were proud that he became one of us.

Conrad was a writer who especially appealed to painters. I can remember a time in those very early days when, besides the few literary connoisseurs who recognised his genius, most of his admirers in England seemed to be painters. And no wonder, for he literally painted with words in those earlier books. His visualising force was extraordinary, and only equalled by his native power of expression.

But I must not weary you further with these English sounds. Conrad was very good to me, very dear to me. One of the greatest writers, one of the most fascinating of men, he will always be a binding link between your country and my country, your Literature and ours.

Speech at the Conrad Memorial, Cracow

I count it great good fortune that my wife and I are allowed to witness this ceremony in memory of him who was for over thirty years our greatest and dearest friend in the writing world. To see this beautiful old city—Conrad's native town—is in itself a great privilege for us who so often heard him speak of it. However much Conrad's love of the sea, of adventure, and of his adopted country led him away from Poland, he remained at heart an attached son of his native land. Here, in the soil of an old culture, the roots of his natural gifts of expression found rich early nourishment. Here he first read Dickens, and those voyages of old explorers, such as Captain Cook, Livingstone, and Franklin, that were the first links between him and England. Here he came again just before the war—which gave to his loved Poland once more the breath of independence. We in England owe a great debt to Cracow in that she gave us one who brought to English Letters something quite new; a richness of colouring, a variety of phrase, and a subtlety of conception such as we had not before he came to us. I once wrote: "He is the only writer of late years who will enrich English Literature to any extent." By that I meant that he brought to us a new temperament, a new way of looking at men and things, a new richness of expression.

A Slav, thinking equally well in Polish, French and English, but expressing himself wholly in the English language, you can readily see what a strange and important event to English Literature his work has been. Alas, that it is finished! Alas, that he has gone from us! We shall not readily again see a writer so loyal, so warmly and widely human in his sympathies, nor one whose vision and gifts of expression were so deep and forceful. A great son of Poland, a great adopted son to England; he will go down the centuries honoured and remembered in both our countries.

1930.

Preface to Conrad's Plays

CONRAD's three plays, *One Day More, Laughing Anne,* and *The Secret Agent,* are all adaptations from stories, and the two in this volume have, curiously enough, the same main theme—the suffering of a woman capable of self-sacrifice. The fact that they are adaptations from stories makes it the more difficult to answer the usual speculation whether this great novelist could, if he had given his time to the task, have become a great dramatist—a speculation, indeed, somewhat idle. In a writing life of thirty years a man has time for much variety. We know that Conrad had a keen dramatic sense; we know—at least I know— that he had fitful longings to write for the stage. And the fact that he never, in all those years, wrote directly for it is to me proof that his nature recoiled too definitely from the limitations which the stage imposes on word-painting and the subtler efforts of a psychologist. The novel suited his nature better than the play, and he instinctively kept to it. If, through unhappy accident, he had begun by writing for the stage, without having first experienced the wider freedom and tasted the more exquisite savour of the novel, he would probably have become one of the greatest dramatists of our time. But we should have lost by it, for, as a novelist, he was in many respects unique.

The process of adaptation is, generally, fatal to the achievement of a stage masterpiece; yet in *One Day More* Conrad so nearly achieved a little masterpiece as to show natural aptitude of the highest order.

It is, in some sort, fitting that I should write this little introduction, since that first of his adaptations for the stage was made in my studio workroom on Campden Hill. Conrad worked at one end of it, on *One Day More*, while, at the other end, I was labouring at some atrocity or other. He sat at a table close to the big window, I stood at a desk, with my back to him, and now and then we would stop and exchange lamentations on the miseries of our respective lots.

"My dear fellow," he would say, "this is too horrible for words," for Conrad did not suffer from satisfaction with his own work. Yet *One Day More* gave him a certain pleasure when he had finished it, and he was eager to see it performed.

He wrote from Capri in May 1905: "Another piece of news is that (would you believe it?) the Stage Society wishes to perform *To-morrow* (as it was then called) next June. Colvin wrote me. Several men, and amongst them G. B. Shaw, profess themselves very much struck." They were right to be struck—the little play has a strange and haunting quality, and Old Hagberd, Harry, and Bessie, are impressive creations.

Not being in England when it was performed, I cannot recall what sort of reception it had from the *cognoscenti* of the Stage Society; but it has evidently been too weird and uncompromising a little piece of tragedy for London Town at large.

I do not know when Conrad adapted *Laughing Anne* from the story *Because of the Dollars*, and indeed never read it till I came to write this preface. Demanding in its short life three scene-sets, none of them easy, and the last exceptionally difficult in stage conditions, it has, as yet, I believe, never been performed. It exemplifies that kind of innocence which novelists commonly have as to what will 'go down' on the stage. Conrad probably never realised that a 'man without hands' would be an almost unbearable spectacle; that what you can write about freely cannot always be endured by the living eye. Anyone who has passed over the Bridge of Galata in the old days—which, very likely, are the new days too—and seen what the beggars there offered to one's sense of pity, will appreciate the nausea inspired by that particular deformity. The lighting, too, of the last scene would be most difficult—effects that depend on shudderings grounded in dim light are to be avoided. A moment or two—yes; but a whole scene—no! To read this play, however, is a pleasure. The figures of Davidson, of poor Laughing Anne, of Fector, Bamtz, and the monster without hands, are thoroughly effective; and, except for those physical drawbacks, the play is admirably contrived.

I am tempted to refer here to the longer adaptation of that most impressive novel *The Secret Agent*; for we have therein a salient illustration, not only of the difficulty of adaptation, but of the fundamental difference between novel and drama as a medium for presenting life. *The*

Secret Agent was a novel of atmosphere, a revelation of hidden depths in human nature, and a sort of creation of an underworld. It depended for its triumph on innumerable subtleties, and the fidelity of a sustained mood. Those of us, not many, who work in both forms, know, to a degree not possible, perhaps, to those who work in one, or work in neither, the cruel obstacles which the physical conditions of the stage put in the way of the sustained mood. I would say that the stage, as a faithful vehicle of mood, falls as far short of the novel as the cinema falls short of the stage. All Art admittedly depends on craft, on the sort of devising which we call technique; even the novel, that most liberal and elastic medium, has its own severities, makes its own rigorous demands on ingenuity, dramatic instinct, and selective power—but they are difficulties to be overcome in a strict privacy, by the writer steeped in his mood, camped on his theme without interference. In writing for the stage the cramp of a hundred and one extra influences comes into play, device becomes trick work, selection is dictated to by physical conditions beyond control. The confirmed novelist, accustomed to freedom and his own conscience, is often given to impatience, and a measure of contempt towards even his own writing for the stage. That merely means, as a rule, that he does not realise the basic difference between the two forms. And, however good a novelist such an one may be, he will inevitably be a less good dramatist. A form must 'enthuse' one, as the Americans say, before one can do it justice. One cannot approach the stage successfully without profound respect, and a deep recognition that its conditions are the essentials of an appeal totally distinct from that of the novel.

I do not think that Conrad was ignorant of this—not at all. His shortcomings were due, partly, to the almost insuperable difficulties of adaptation, and, partly, to inadequate mastery of trick work which has to be learned. In other words, he had not given enough time to the dramatic form. He did not quite know how to balance his effects, how to economise his words, or how to keep his line of action clear and inevitable. A little more experience would have shown him, for instance, that the *salon* scene, as written, in his dramatic version of *The Secret Agent*, was dead wood.

I read his adaptation in manuscript before the play was produced, and, in answer to my somewhat critical letter, received one which contained this passage: "The play is purely illustrative. It is because of that illustrative nature that I have let it spread itself into scenes which from the point of action alone may, and obviously do, appear super-fluous and detached from the subject. Whereas to my feeling they are all closely to the point." This is Conrad's defence of the play as it stands. It does not go quite to the root of the matter, for as much feeling and illustrative value as he put into the play would have been preserved, and could even have been increased, by the eliminating of *longueurs*, if his technique had been equal to the task. In other words, if he had given some of the years he gave to the novel to writing drama instead. And, anyway, the mood and illustrative value of his theme did not and could not receive as full expression in the play as it did in the novel.

So that it comes back to this: one is glad he didn't give time enough to play-writing. Those of us who remember that amazing cab drive in the novel—the gem passage of *The Secret Agent*—unrenderable on the stage, realise very well that his time was better concentrated on an unfettered fidelity to his moods in his unflinching scrutiny of men and things, on his power of painting in words, and on a psychological insight unsurpassed for depth and subtlety.

Of the actual production of *The Secret Agent*, which I thought left much to be desired, Conrad wrote with his characteristic generosity: "Now it is all over, my state may be described as that of serene joy, only marred by remorse at the injustice of my past thoughts towards the actors, who had a lot of characters certainly not of a 'stock' kind thrown at their heads just twenty days before the first performance. Now like a man touched by grace, I think of them with actual tenderness and almost with affection . . .

"The disagreeable part of this business is to see wasted the hard work of people who depend on it for their livelihood, and for whom success would mean assured employment and ease of mind. One feels guilty somehow."

There spoke the heart of Conrad, forever in sympathy with men and women who did their job as well as they could, and thinking of others before himself.

1924.

HOMAGE TO ANATOLE FRANCE

ANATOLE FRANCE is gone, the greatest writer of our time.

He was the supreme example of what can be achieved by one whose gift of expression has been trained and tempered to the perfect service of an unique mind. His pen was a sword-blade, ever drawn, so lambent and so fine that it played, invisible, like a wind, through the ribs of "Civilisation."

He was never in a pose, yet he was always at an angle. Blandest, yet most genuine and poignant of ironists, he was the destroying angel of all that is crude and vulgar, brutal, narrow and insensitive.

Among English writers his influence was great. Flaubert, de Maupassant, Anatole France—of the three he was most potent. The power of such a writer is proportioned by the value of his temperament to the Age he lives in. There has never been an age that so needed an Anatole

France. Deep learning, wide and humane thinking, self-sacrificing craftsmanship, and an exquisite sense of balance, he had all that the age has not.

His country may restore her devastated areas, our country may regain her markets, the car of material Progress may once more exceed the speed limit, but that living spiritual protest, that fine quivering flame, whom we call Anatole France, has burned out, and we shall not see its like again.

1924.

JOHN MASEFIELD AND HIS NARRATIVE POEMS

WHEN in November appeared that amazing poem, "The Everlasting Mercy," the chorus of comment was of due warmth and enthusiasm. Now that *The English Review* of February publishes "The Widow in the Bye Street," it is the more surprising to me that little notice has been taken of the event. For assuredly this narrative poem by no whit falls short of its predecessor. I have called the appearance of the poem an event. And when an event happens it is a pity that people should not know of it. In the spirit of the town-crier, then, I take up my pen.

*   *   *   *   *

As with good ships, and with good wine, it is sometimes long before a writer with elements of greatness finds himself—finds the exact form that shall best express the best within him. Though in *The Tragedy of Nan* John Masefield wrote a play with much beauty and much strength, it seems to me that not until he invented in these two narrative poems a form absolutely his own did he achieve complete felicity in the expression of a temperament unique among living writers. There come moments (I speak of those long creative moments that last, perhaps, months) when by some beneficent chance—in reality no chance if we could see below the surface—all the qualities in a man lose antagonism, rush together, blend, and work in furious harmony to some well-nigh perfect achievement. These two poems are, I feel, the result of one of these long creative moments. They have the same original form, capturing reality in terms of romance, and a particular quality—not, I think, yet pointed out—which for want of a better word I must call growth. They are not "made" things. They spring, vision by vision, thought by thought, with a certain fateful sureness, out of an overmastering mood. One feels from line to line that they could not be otherwise. And this is the greatest quality in a work of art. They remind one of sculpture, rather rough, but rough with the rugged, ragged, yet utter coherence of life running into its appointed shape. They have the epic feeling, never present in work epically resolved on. And they are strange—stranger, I fancy, than Chorus thinks; there is nothing to compare them with; for they have not bothered themselves with tradition, æsthetics, art, and all the rest of it. They have brooded and sung themselves into being. And so they have their blemishes, scars, and weak endings, and all those petty disfigurements abhorrent to indoor taste, but they have real blood in their veins, and real marrow in their bones.

*   *   *   *   *

I have said that "The Widow in the Bye Street" is at least the equal of "The Everlasting Mercy." I wish to make no unprofiting comparison; but while I feel that the

second poem has not quite the same leap and force of narrative expression as the first, it is superior in conception,
higher in mood; nor has it any confusion between the soul
of the hero and his creator, such as mars a little the last part
of "The Everlasting Mercy." For Saul Kane—such is the
nature of his kind—would have been as violent in his conversion as in his old unregenerate days, incapable of that
particular new skin with which the poem invests him. "The
Widow in the Bye Street" touches, therefore, the higher
point of inevitability. It escapes, too, the charge of ab-
normality in theme which might captiously be brought
against "The Everlasting Mercy." They are both, it is
true, dramas of change; but the earlier poem sets out
the rare case, the latter poem is an illustration far more
universal, of the fate which the life force coils round human lives; the fate which lurks, waiting but for the fa-
vouring moment—sometimes, mercifully, never reached—
to leap out and destroy. The only shaft, not merely a pro-
fessional toy shaft, which can be discharged at this poem,
is to say that it leaves a faint uncertainty as to whether the
central theme is the destruction of the poor old mother, or
the destroying power on all around of such a woman as
Anna. But this, I think, is the hypercriticism of after-
thought, not of the fresh and certain first impression. The
march of the narrative is clear, and perfectly assured; it
never halts, and it never breaks into the artificial or the
self-conscious; it catches and moulds the real life, feelings,
and words of real people, presenting them so that you cannot, as it were, get beneath, or go further back than the
words which reveal the pulses of these creatures, and clothe
the thoughts which leave their souls. The projection of
these simple and raw folk is made in the only right and
true terms of their raw simplicity. This is in itself a fine
feat; but it is not this which makes the poem great. It is
great in that there has been woven into it, rhythmically and

without violence or sense of artifice, a dirge-like quality
which lifts it into the Greek mood. I cannot render this
chiming, dirging spirit—the very name and breath of the
poem—in any other way than by quoting some of the pas-
sages through which it is conveyed.

> So the four souls are ranged, the chess-board set,
> The dark, invisible hand of Secret Fate
> Brought it to come to being that they met
> After so many years of lying in wait.
> While we least think it he prepares his Mate.
> Mate and the King's pawn played, it never ceases,
> Though all the earth is dust of taken pieces.
>
> All the tides triumph when the white moon fills.
> Down in the race the toppling waters shout,
> The breakers shake the bases of the hills,
> There is a thundering where the streams go out,
> And the wise shipman puts his ship about,
> Seeing the gathering of those waters wan,
> But what when love makes high tide in a man? . . .
>
> Love is a flame to burn out human wills,
> Love is a flame to set the will on fire,
> Love is a flame to cheat men into mire.
>
> Man cannot call the brimming instant back;
> Time's an affair of instants spun to days;
> If man must make an instant gold, or black,
> Let him, he may, but Time must go his ways.
> Life may be duller for an instant's blaze.
> Life's an affair of instants spun to years,
> Instants are only cause of all these tears. . . .
>
> > Heartless is ever swift at making friends,
> > Heartless plucks honey from the evil time,
> > The heartless soul makes many bells to chime:
> > Joybells and deathbells, wedding bells and dirges,
> > Heartless is one of God's appointed scourges.

*   *   *   *   *

And those lines telling of the widow's lost singing, with which the poem ends:

> Till with full throat, over the hills away,
> They lift it clear, oh, very clear it towers
> Mixed with the swish of many falling flowers.

*   *   *   *   *

If there be in our time a poem written that has this triumphant dirge-like beauty I have yet to know it.

1912.

NOTE ON 'THE PORTRAIT OF A LADY'
(HENRY JAMES)

THIS novel may be likened to a dish of fine tea that, set before a mental epicure, steals his approval with its aroma. It is to be sniffed before drinking, and drunk out of thin china, not at a draught. And the novel has on the faculties the same effect as tea. It stirs them, frees, and cools; it stimulates a gentle perspiration, a sense of curiosity, and of an unconscious intellectual mastery. After sipping this clear and fragrant liquid, we try to unravel subtleties which, when not thus delicately intoxicated, we leave alone.

In a world where unconsciousness is highly prized, and 'to meddle with the works' esteemed somewhat useless, books like this are rare, disconcerting, and neglected—for goodness' sake give us beer or wine instead—let us even drink Zoedone, rather than a fluid that sets the spirit buzzing. In plain words, the book is delicate, so delicate that flesh and blood is but suggested, as a laurel-bush is suggested by its shadow on a lawn. In reading it we pass our time among shadows—cunningly outlined, shadows deliberately created of people seen with the fine reflective eye—a gallery full of them.

Mr. and Mrs. Touchett; Ralph Touchett; Pansy Osmond, and her father; Caspar Goodwood; Henriette Stacpole; Madame Merle; Mr. Bantling; Edward Rosier; and—the Lady. They vary in merit, both as types and in presentation, but their quality is unmistakable; subtle, swift, sure, soul-like; they are all shadows drawn by one constitutionally averse to the corporeal. To Lord Warburton's body we come a trifle closer, perhaps because of all the lot he alone is not American.

This incorporeality is inveterate, and suavely delightful. But since the main theme of the book is the sexual attraction, however disguised, of one woman for four men, we could have pardoned her creator for giving his heroine a little more body.

The portrait of this lady, with manifold lights, and countless lines, appears wholly to the mind. The attempt is generous and complex, amazing in fertility and romance, touching in its sincerity, freedom, and the whole-hearted surrender of the painter to his work. The tints are beautifully selected, the lines beautifully traced, a spirit has been breathed over them, and yet—! The very ardour has been a little fatal to the brush work.

The portrait of the Lady is at once the best and worst thing in the book; best, because breathed on more largely, and better revealing the painter's intellectual mastery; worst, because least reduced to the earthly proportions that more sharply hit our sensuous perceptions. In the cant of the writing table, it is very nearly, but not quite 'done'— as, for example, Irena in Turgenev's *Smoke* is done. Something is wanting to this almost breathing shadow; the seductive something that lays a spell over criticism, the sensuous something which would show us that which intellectualism, however subtle, however honest, will never make us see quite plainly. But it is a great attempt, and, if for nothing but delicacy, deserves to rank among the blessed.

The silken spinning of Isabel's relations with her four suitors—what a lesson in the unobvious! The reawakening in Lord Warburton after she is married to Osmond, and her perception of it—could presentation be more cunning? Innumerable pages, eulogistic or carping, might be written on this portrait, but nothing would sweep away the generosity of the design or the taste of its execution. Better to raise side issues.

What is Isabel's significance in the modern world? We suspect her portrayer of attempting the picture of high, but not quite immaculate, American girlhood; just as in Madame de Mauve he painted with sympathy high, and quite immaculate American girlhood; and in Daisy Miller, with pathos, the low and non-immaculate type. The pure fire of Western idealism is alight within Isabel Archer, and within Madame de Mauve. Narrow at the wick, broadening, and at summit fining again to a point, it seems to exist without a fear of going out; in Madame de Mauve steady and straight and low; in Isabel impetuous and free—for the one has little vitality, the other much.

Thus Isabel Archer is significant. In her something in the American soul is concreted—that something which differentiates it from the Latin and the Slav and even from the English soul. In Isabel Archer's aspiring, restless sympathy, in her craving for refined knowledge, there is no trace of that realistic acceptance which is the keynote of the Latin, or of that avid drinking-in of sensation which is at the root of the Slav soul. In her aspiration, sympathy, and craving, is an element, too, more flighty, less mellow, and less dreamy, than in ourselves. She is best American of the best Americans—as they were in the nineteenth century, a priestess of their peculiar flame.

And a second side issue: Has an author the right to set a conundrum in his last three pages?

The 'Lady' is married to Osmond—to Osmond, the very

type of repellent egoism; Goodwood, strong, silent and devoted, has kissed her. We are told that his kiss reached her senses; and then that she saw "a very straight path." Two days later Goodwood is informed by Henriette that Isabel has started for Rome (and Osmond). He is cast down.

" 'Just you wait!' said Henriette. Goodwood looked up at her."

We are told not any more. Now, either the just uncertainty of our minds is due to a technical error, some omitted sentence of illumination, which is pardonable in any but a great master; or we are deliberately left to choose our own end, which is quite unpardonable in even a great master. The ultimate touch, in fact, is missing. We do not know, we have to guess, what the 'Lady' is going to do. The circumstances have been crescendoed to the final exposition of character, we are face to face with the crucial test, and—we are left!

Our belief is that Isabel, not being Madame de Mauve, ended by joining Goodwood; but what is the author's?

PREFACE TO 'GREEN MANSIONS'
(W. H. HUDSON)

I TAKE up pen for this foreword with the fear of one who knows that he cannot do justice to his subject, and the trembling of one who would not, for a good deal, set down words unpleasing to the eye of him who wrote *Green Mansions, The Purple Land*, and all those other books which have meant so much to me. For of all living authors—now that Tolstoi has gone—I could least dispense with W. H. Hudson. Why do I love his writing so? I think because he is, of living writers that I read, the rarest spirit, and has the clearest gift of conveying to me the nature of that spirit. Writers are to their readers little new worlds to be explored; and each traveller in the realms of literature must needs have a favourite hunting ground, which, in his good will—or perhaps merely in his egoism—he would wish others to share with him.

The great and abiding misfortunes of most of us writers are twofold: We are, as worlds, rather common tramping ground for our readers, rather tame territory; and as guides and dragomans thereto we are too superficial, lacking clear intimacy of expression; in fact—like guide or dragoman— we cannot let folk into the real secrets, or show them the spirit, of the land.

Now Hudson, whether in a pure romance like this *Green Mansions*, or in that romantic piece of realism *The Purple Land*, or in books like *Idle Days in Patagonia*, *Afoot in England*, *The Land's End*, *Adventures Among Birds*, *A Shepherd's Life*, and all his other nomadic records of communings with men, birds, beasts, and Nature, has a supreme gift of disclosing not only the thing he sees but the spirit of his vision. Without apparent effort he takes you with him into a rare, free, natural world, and always you are refreshed, stimulated, enlarged, by going there.

He is of course a distinguished naturalist, probably the most acute, broad-minded, and understanding observer of Nature, living. And this, in an age of specialism, which loves to put men into pigeon-holes and label them, has been a misfortune to the reading public, who seeing the label Naturalist, pass on and take down the nearest novel. Hudson has indeed the gifts and knowledge of a Naturalist, but that is a mere fraction of his value and interest. A really great writer such as this is no more to be circumscribed by a single word than America by the part of it called New York. The expert knowledge which Hudson has of Nature gives to all his work backbone and surety of fibre, and to his sense of beauty an intimate actuality. But his real eminence and extraordinary attraction lie in his

spirit and philosophy. We feel from his writings that he
is nearer to Nature than other men, and yet more truly civilised. The competitive, towny culture, the queer up-to-
date commercial knowingness with which we are so busy
coating ourselves, simply will not stick to him. A passage
in his *Hampshire Days* describes him better than I can:
"The blue sky, the brown soil beneath, the grass, the trees,
the animals, the wind, and rain, and stars are never strange
to me; for I am in and of and am one with them; and
my flesh and the soil are one, and the heat in my blood and
in the sunshine are one, and the winds and the tempests and
my passions are one. I feel the 'strangeness' only with regard to my fellow-men, especially in towns, where they
exist in conditions unnatural to me, but congenial to them.
. . . In such moments we sometimes feel a kinship with,
and are strangely drawn to, the dead, who were not as
these; the long, long dead, the men who knew not life in
towns, and felt no strangeness in sun and wind and rain."
This unspoiled unity with Nature pervades all his writings;
they are remote from the fret and dust and pettiness of
town life; they are large, direct, free. It is not quite simplicity, for the mind of this writer is subtle and fastidious,
sensitive to each motion of natural and human life; but his
sensitiveness is somehow different from, almost inimical to,
that of us others, who sit indoors and dip our pens in shades
of feeling. Hudson's fancy is akin to the flight of the birds
that are his special loves—it never seems to have entered a
house, but since birth to have been roaming the air, in rain
and sun, or visiting the trees and the grass. I not only dis-
believe utterly, but intensely dislike, the doctrine of metemp-
sychosis, which, if I understand it aright, seems the nega-
tion of the creative impulse, an apotheosis of staleness—
nothing quite new in the world, never anything quite new
—not even the soul of a baby; and so I am not prepared
to entertain the whim that a bird was one of his remote

incarnations; still, in sweep of wing, quickness of eye, and natural sweet strength of song he is not unlike a super-bird —which is a horrid image.

And that reminds me: This, after all, is a foreword to *Green Mansions*—the romance of the bird-girl Rima—a story actual yet fantastic, which immortalises, I think, as passionate a love of all beautiful things as ever was in the heart of man. Somewhere Hudson says: "The sense of the beautiful is God's best gift to the human soul." So it is; and to pass that gift on to others, in such measure as herein is expressed, must surely have been happiness to him who wrote *Green Mansions*. In form and spirit the book is unique, a simple romantic narrative transmuted by sheer glow of beauty into a prose poem. Without ever departing from its quality of a tale, it symbolises the yearning of the human soul for the attainment of perfect love and beauty in this life—that impossible perfection which we must all learn to see fall from its high tree and be consumed in the flames, as was Rima the bird-girl, but whose fine white ashes we gather that they may be mingled at last with our own, when we too have been refined by the fire of death's resignation. The book is soaked through and through with a strange beauty. I will not go on singing its praises, or trying to make it understood, because I have other words to say of its author.

Do we realise how far our town life and culture have got away from things that really matter; how instead of making civilisation our handmaid to freedom we have set her heel on our necks, and under it bite dust all the time? Hudson, whether he knows it or not, is now the chief standard-bearer of another faith. Thus he spake in *The Purple Land*: "Ah, yes, we are all vainly seeking after happiness in the wrong way. It was with us once and ours, but we despised it, for it was only the old common happiness which Nature gives to all her children, and we went away from it in search of another grander kind of happiness which some dreamer—Bacon or another —assured us we should find. We had only to conquer Nature, find out her secrets, make her our obedient slave, then the Earth would be Eden, and every man Adam and every woman Eve. We are still marching bravely on, conquering Nature, but how weary and sad we are getting! The old joy in life and gaiety of heart have vanished, though we do sometimes pause for a few moments in our long forced march to watch the labours of some pale mechanician, seeking after perpetual motion, and indulge in a little, dry, cackling laugh at his expense." And again: "For here the religion that languishes in crowded cities or steals shame-faced to hide itself in dim churches, flourishes greatly, filling the soul with a solemn joy. Face to face with Nature on the vast hills at eventide, who does not feel himself near to the Unseen?

> "Out of his heart God shall not pass
> His image stampèd is on every grass."

All Hudson's books breathe this spirit of revolt against our new enslavement by towns and machinery, and are true Oases in an Age so dreadfully resigned to the "pale mechanician."

But Hudson is not, as Tolstoi was, a conscious prophet; his spirit is freer, more wilful, whimsical—almost perverse —and far more steeped in love of beauty. If you called him a prophet he would stamp his foot at you—as he will at me if he reads these words; but his voice is prophetic, for all that, crying in a wilderness, out of which, at the call, will spring up roses here and there, and the sweet-smelling grass. I would that every man, woman, and child in England were made to read him. He is a tonic, a deep refreshing drink, with a strange and wonderful flavour; he is a mine of new interests, and ways of thought instinc-

tively right. As a simple narrator he is well-nigh unsurpassed; as a stylist he has few, if any, living equals. And
in all his work there is an indefinable freedom from any
thought of after-benefit—even from the desire that we
should read him. He puts down what he sees and feels, out
of sheer love of the thing seen, and the emotion felt; the
smell of the lamp has not touched a single page that he ever
wrote. That alone is a marvel to us who know that to
write well, even to write clearly, is a woundy business, long
to learn, hard to learn, and no gift of the angels. Style
should not obtrude between a writer and his reader; it
should be servant, not master. To use words so true and
simple, that they oppose no obstacle to the flow of thought
and feeling from mind to mind, and yet by juxtaposition
of word-sounds set up in the recipient continuing emotion
or gratification—this is the essence of style; and Hudson's
writing has pre-eminently this double quality. From almost
any page of his books an example might be taken. Here is
one no better than a thousand others, a description of two
little girls on a beach: "They were dressed in black frocks
and scarlet blouses, which set off their beautiful small dark
faces; their eyes sparkled like black diamonds, and their
loose hair was a wonder to see, a black mist or cloud about
their heads and necks composed of threads fine as gossamer,
blacker than jet and shining like spun glass—hair that
looked as if no comb or brush could ever tame its beautiful
wildness. And in spirit they were what they seemed: such
a wild, joyous, frolicsome spirit, with such grace and fleet-
ness, one does not look for in human beings, but only in
birds or in some small bird-like volatile mammal—a squir-
rel or a spider-monkey of the tropical forest, or the chin-
chilla of the desolate mountain slopes; the swiftest, wild-
est, loveliest, most airy and most vocal of small beasties."
Or this, as the quintessence of a sly remark: "After that
Manuel got on to his horse and rode away. It was black

and rainy, but he had never needed moon or lantern to find what he sought by night, whether his own house, or a fat cow—also his own, perhaps." So one might go on quoting felicity for ever from this writer. He seems to touch every string with fresh and uninked fingers; and the secret of his power lies, I suspect, in the fact that his words: "Life being more than all else to me . . ." are so utterly true.

I do not descant on his love for simple folk and simple things, his championship of the weak, and the revolt against the cagings and cruelties of life, whether to men or birds or beasts, that springs out of him as if against his will; because, having spoken of him as one with a vital philosophy or faith, I don't wish to draw red herrings across the main trail of his worth to the world. His work is a vision of natural beauty and of human life as it might be, quickened and sweetened by the sun and the wind and the rain, and by fellowship with all the other forms of life—the truest vision now being given to us, who are more in want of it than any generation has ever been. A very great writer; and—to my thinking—the most valuable our Age possesses.

1915.

NOTE ON W. H. HUDSON

WITH the passing out of W. H. Hudson the English-speaking world, perhaps the wide world, has lost its most unique personality. This is said deliberately out of some little knowledge of personalities and the world. He is quite irreplaceable. Happily, his work preserves for us his rare spirit and strange charm. I, who only knew him for twenty-four years, can of course remember him only as a man of mature age, for he was eighty when he died last month; but I can well credit the impression he made on those who knew him in youth and middle age. A very tall man—quite six feet two—with raven-black hair, a cast of feature that always reminded one of an eagle, and wonderful deep brown eyes; a fine horseman, a great walker; absolutely unself-conscious, independent, and original, I have heard old people describe him as the most striking figure they ever saw; indeed, he was that to the end of his days.

Other men, however remarkable in their different ways, one can always relate to some known category of this world, but Hudson had a special quality which eluded classification——he seemed to have slipped through to us from somewhere quite different. Not that he was primitive, or what is called "a child of Nature," for he was extraordinarily subtle, one of the best-read men of the age and one of the deepest and most varied thinkers; but he was wrought of fibre spiritually simpler and yet more wise than *homo sapiens*. He reminded me of an embodiment of Nature which by accident had got entangled in our civilisation. I can imagine that Leonardo da Vinci gave the people of his day something of the same "beyond-his-world" feeling.

*   *   *   *   *

A writer in the London *Nation* has pointed out very aptly the reason why Hudson's extraordinary blend of gifts has stood in the way of his popularity and fame: He was too preoccupied with Nature for our literary folk, too much of an artist for our scientific naturalists. Edward Garnett in his *Friday Nights* interpreted justly the unique value of Hudson's gifts when he said that we can never understand Nature unless we realise her emotionally. No man, I think, has ever realized Nature emotionally so completely as Hudson, and no writer has been so able to pass on to others that emotional realisation. The very simplicity and intimacy of his prose, this singular faculty of giving to his reader thought and feeling free from all barrier of style, hides from that reader, as it were, the greatness of his achievement. The self-conscious æstheticism of Richard Jefferies, the precise factual merits of Gilbert White make more impression on average readers; but their real triumph is as nothing to Hudson's. Jefferies as an artist was not his equal, White as a precise naturalist was no better, and he had not Hudson's range of experience and knowledge; while in the mere writing of prose Hudson at his best was the best of the three. Whether or no popularity comes now that he is gone, his fame is as certain as the occupation of one who grows wheat for our eating. Nature will last our time, nor shall we put aside as *vieux jeu* him who can best tell us her long story.

England, the United States, the Argentine go shares in Hudson. His father was of Devonshire stock from——he has told me——Clyst, near Exeter; his mother of a New England family; the land of his birth and upbringing was the Argentine. One never saw him without thinking a little of old Spain, and of Indian horsemen sitting motionless gazing out over great spaces. His talk, which had no brilliancy, was yet the most truly original I have ever listened to, and it is quite wrong to speak of him as "slightly lacking in humour"; his sense of humour was very strong, but as peculiar and individual as everything else about him. No man I have known set less store by this world's goods; he quite unaffectedly preferred to be poor, and poor he was almost to the end.

To speak of his love——his infatuation, some would call it——for birds, beasts, and flowers is merely to sum up the whole spirit of his books and tell the tale of his spring, his summer, his autumn, and his winter; but birds came first with him. In their songs and quick, airy movements he had perhaps the sense of escape from a world to which he only partly belonged——that escape which in *Green Mansions* he pictured with such word magic. The remarkable consistency of Hudson's life has escaped direct notice. The tastes, habits, affections, almost the beliefs, of his last years in Cornwall and London were practically the same as those of the little boy on the pampas seventy years ago. Never, I should think, was a life lived in stranger single-heartedness. It was this natural unself-conscious devotion of his to Nature, undeviating and unfanatical, which surrounds his figure with a certain mystery and attracts to it a sort of reverence in this so parti-coloured world careful and troubled about many things.

Of his books I have most love for *Far Away and Long Ago*, for *The Purple Land*, *El Ombú* (that great short story) for *Green Mansions*, *Afoot in England*, and *A Shepherd's Life*——probably because the artist in him takes, in those books, distinct precedence over the naturalist. But, in truth, to compare one book of Hudson's with another is much like dissecting the parts of a bird's flight. He was the fortunate writer in that he found the way, for which we all grope, to give his very self expression in all that he wrote.

Full of prejudices, but without rancours, full of whims, Victorianly unemotional in manner and in his deliberate speech, with a perversity as amusing and a malice as harmless as that of a big dog; with a great love of beauty, a delight in children and in music, with a disconcerting power of penetration into the heart of a matter, and the curiosity of a born observer, with the zest and the melancholy of an intense lover of life; careless of comfort and indifferent to danger, yet inherently wary; with a deep core to his heart beneath a crusty surface——he was, indeed, rich material.

His memory was wonderful. I remember his saying: "We remember what we are interested in." If that be so, he was interested in many things. I have heard it said of him that he was a Bedouin in a tent, forever packing it up and moving on. Not so! He dwelled, quiet and constant, in the tent of his devotion, while around him the sands of our modern life eddied and swirled.

I am glad to think he finished his last book. It was to

be, if I remember, on a subject very deep—the Nature origins of music. He who had been listening-in to Nature all his life must have heard secrets worth telling us about the beginnings of the first art.

I am glad to think he died in his sleep without the pang of a good-bye.

As a rule I do not worship heroes—no rule but has its exception.

1924.

NOTE ON EDWARD GARNETT

In the brief, but wide, searching, and sympathetic study of Tolstoy that Edward Garnett has contributed to Constable's Modern Biographies, he has insisted first and foremost on the necessity for remembering the many-sidedness of Tolstoy, for not losing sight of the war between the artist and the moralist, that was always being waged, and the fusion of them that was always going on in his colossal spirit. "The religious fanaticism of a suffering and questioning nature was doubled in Tolstoy with the personality of a joyously vital, richly sensuous 'pagan prince.'" Let us not—Mr. Garnett in effect says—to the marriage of these twain true minds admit impediment! He is right. If, to remembrance that Tolstoy's vitality was terrific, that his love of sheer truthfulness has never been surpassed, we add Dostoievsky's dictum that he was "one of those Russian minds which can only see that which is before their eyes," we begin to get understanding of a nature that ever lived and worked at full pressure, and was never at peace. We begin to realise how—just as all Nature is the result of the clash and fusion of opposing principles, so was the great nature and work of him whom, however one may love and admire Turgenev, and stand amazed at Dostoievsky, I, at all events, must think the greatest of the Russians.

But I am not reviewing a book by Tolstoy, I am reviewing a critical study of him by Edward Garnett, and I am going frankly to take this opportunity of saying what I think of Edward Garnett as a critic; because I feel too few people have any adequate idea of how very deeply Mr. Garnett has affected the currents and trend of imaginative work in our time.

I say without hesitation that he has done more for English fiction than any living critic, and for less recognition. It is devoutly to be hoped that he, who was born with such distrust of success, with such inveterate feeling for the lost cause, will forgive me for thus expressing my conviction; for I cannot help saying at last what justice should have said long ago.

During the past twenty years and more Edward Garnett has "discovered" more talent, helped more aspiration, and fought more battles for the cause of good literature than anyone who can be named; and he has done it nearly all in the dark, and all for love of the real thing. He has never turned aside, never been swayed a hair's breadth by the tides of popular feeling; he has had his own vision and been true to it. Often and often he has howled in a wilderness the unknown names of those now seated in high places. (Let me not howl them now, lest I remind the great that they once were not!) Still more often he has set his single lance in rest against shoddy, and the ranks of mere popularity. In all this, what—apart from his courage and independence—has been his gift? This, I think: He, almost alone among English critics of fiction, has had the faculty of giving himself up completely to the book before him, of letting the work print itself upon him with the directness and fidelity of photography. He has brought to the pictures of fiction a clear surface of extraordinary sensitiveness on which extravagances and distortions of line can be seen engraved in their true ugliness. This is a great and very rare faculty, and to maintain it so unimpaired year after year among the welter of books is little short of marvellous. Criticism, of course, is very much an affair of temperament, and according to our natures we must all differ, but what makes one man a real critic and another only a licensed pronouncer of opinions is just that exceedingly rare faculty of ploughing up your surface afresh, and watering it with hope, ready for each new book, always believing that you are going to find something good, something that will crown letters with delight, and, revealing the springs of life, make for the enrichment of art and knowledge. Edward Garnett has, it seems to me, always wanted to find something good, always made himself ready; but he has never compromised with his instincts, never persuaded himself that what he did not like was good, or feared to justify and champion what he did like. It is twenty years since that quiet little revolution in English fiction began with our first knowledge of the Russians, through Constance Garnett's translations of Turgenev, and Edward Garnett's prefaces thereto. Now, the peculiar quality, the one quality in which the Russians excel all other writers of fiction, is spiritual truthfulness, a sort of natural power of putting forth impressions and experience unstained by self-consciousness. It is this quality which Edward Garnett seems to have been born to nurse and foster; and his incessant championship in the face of the solemn oppositions and false romanticism has vitally contributed to the sincerity and revealing force of modern English fiction. He has been the lifelong enemy of inflation, the lifelong friend of truth delicately recorded. There has been no critic of our time with a keener appreciation, not for style—to which he is, indeed, to my mind, too indifferent—but for form; no critic to whom the naked line of the tree has been so visible through the enshrouding foliage; none who has been more surely able to say: This or that is an excrescence. And this instinct of his exercised in the many subtle ways open to a critic and lover of books has been of peculiar value to the fiction-writers of a nation celebrated for its adherence to form in conduct, notorious for its indifference to form in art.

I can well imagine, for example, what the upturned attitude of the British man of letters' nose would have been twenty years ago to those little marvels of form, those little breaths of truth, Tchehov's short stories. To-day the attitude of that nose is one of savouring delight, and the change is due more to Edward Garnett than to any man alive; not because he has written much, if at all, of Tchehov, but because he has had the power of distilling year by year into the minds of others his unerring feeling for what is the right shape and clothing of idea and incident. From time immemorial it has been the fashion of British fiction, fortified by British criticism, to think that it does not much matter how a thing is said, a story told, so long as it is told. Into this fashion Edward Garnett's instinctive horror of inflation and irrelevance has cut with a depth that few perhaps realise. The value of a real critic is not to be measured by his actual writings, but by the force of his personality, persistently expressed in many ways that do not leap to the eye. There is a strange potency in that half-hidden figure, standing so firm on the base of an instinct and conviction which never swerves. It is a lighthouse hardly seen by the landsmen public, known only to us navigators of the shoals and cross-currents of fiction.

Freedom may be the essence of imagination, but it is vital to have here and there the guidance of some piercing insight into what is true imagination, and what is its essential clothing. However much we fiction writers are inclined to shut our eyes to what may be destructive of our pet luxuriances, every now and then we open them, and there is the lamp, only visible to us, perhaps, but none the less invaluable for that.

The novelist is nowadays very much in the glare of the footlights; we come in for all the shekels and the hand-shakes. Those who, year after year—they are not many—who for sheer love of Letters help and guide us, come in for little but our carpings.

To Edward Garnett we owe a great debt, that perhaps cannot be paid. There are some men born to give out sympathy and help to others, and to forget themselves. They have reward, but it is seldom coined.

Truly, it is an odd comment upon the values of life, that, when a man is self-forgetful, when his love for what he does surpasses his love for himself, he is generally found to be more or less effaced. Here is one who has never beaten upon a tenpenny drum. How many are there, I wonder, who know his real worth!

1914.

FOREWORD TO JEANNE D'ARC
(PLAY BY EDWARD GARNETT)

FOREWORDS do not sell books; on the contrary—they only irritate critics. Why, then, publishers should be so anxious to obtain them, no one knows, certainly not this writer.

I will confine my words to the *Trial of Jeanne d'Arc*. I am told that this play was described as a 'misfire.' If you go to a play, no matter what the subject, hoping to be made to laugh, if you expect a dramatist to convert the most tragic of historical themes into a vehicle that shall bear him to greater heights of popular esteem, if indeed, whatever the ailment, you desire 'the mixture as before,' then, I suppose, the trial of Jeanne d'Arc was a 'misfire.'

If, on the other hand, a subject carries with it the need

of treatment adjusted to its essence rather than a treatment which shall save one from appreciating what its essence was, then I submit that whoever saw the play and came away and wrote the word 'misfire' is one of those who should have been drowned at birth.

I did not expect, or wish to be amused; I knew that the author cared no kick for popular esteem, that he was indifferent to ailments, and void of mixtures; that he had sunk himself in the documentation of the trial; and that in Jean Forbes-Robertson he had secured the only young English actress fitted for the part of Jeanne.

Admitting that the audience, at the few performances which were given, was always of a serious temper, it was impressive to watch their attitude throughout. The word 'misfire' had not occurred to them. They sat in a sort of comfortless reverence, and though I should have expected them to say now and again: 'I seem to have heard that before,' or: 'Enough about these voices,' they did not. They were not amused, but they were absorbed and carried back into the atmosphere of the time.

Watching the play, I realised, as never before, how fatal to the full current of emotion constant change of scene can be; and the last scene was ruined by the procession to the execution passing in front of the group who have been watching its formation. Essential that we should see that procession beyond, and as it were, with their eyes. In spite of these defects the staging on the whole was good, and plunged one far back into medievalism; it preserved the single-hearted emotion of the play clear and tense from start to finish; and thereby one received a coherent view of the gallant and tortured Jeanne. I will confess that the culmination moment came after the play was over, when the actress re-appeared to take our plaudits. While she stood there, silent and suffering, the still dignity of her young face and figure was a perfect tribute to the sincere and sustained emotion that the play had exacted from her. A dramatist for once had known when to stop.

circa 1928.

NOTE ON MEGGIE ALBANESI

MEGGIE ALBANESI: I only saw her play seven parts in all; Jill in *The Skin Game*, Wanda in *The First and the Last*, Mabel in *Loyalties*, Lady Jane in *Shall we join the Ladies?* Sidney in *A Bill of Divorcement*, Trelawney in the first act of *Trelawney of the Wells*, and the twin in *The Lilies of the Field*; and yet her death gives me a sense of eclipse. It is as if the Dark Remover had filched the brightest, steadiest little lantern of all.

Her technique was good and clean, for she was trained under Helen Haye, that past-mistress of sure effects; her individuality was exceptionally strong, yet I think would never have crystallised into just-Meggie Albanesi on the stage; she had real devotion to her art, great quickness to seize shades of meaning, and a brain which she did not hesitate to use.

But none of these qualities, nor all of them together, account for just the sense of loss that her death brings. She had a curious and unique faculty of emotional truth. I never saw her (and I watched her through some sixty rehearsals) fumble, blur, or falsify an emotional effect. She struck instantaneously and as if from her heart, the right note of feeling. Those who have had much to do with play production alone will understand how excessively rare such a quality is. For me, her most beautiful achievement as a whole, was her Polish girl Wanda in *The First and the Last*. I could never watch that except through a certain mist. But I think that she reached her highest pitch of emotional truth in the final scene of *A Bill of Divorce-*

ment. In both those plays, indeed, she passed quite beyond acting.

There was never any doubt about her effects, the edges of her impersonations were so clean-cut; each movement and each phrase carried over to one—clear, decisive. As 'Jill,' as 'Lady Jane,' as 'the twin,' she marked quite definitely her delicate sense of comedy. She was not limited. She would have gone very far.

Not often does Death so wastefully spill.

1924.

NOTE ON R. B. CUNNINGHAME GRAHAM

In these very few words I speak of Cunninghame Graham rather as writer, than as man. His peculiar and quite unique talent has been given so far as I know entirely to short stories, and one book of travels. I confine myself to his short stories, the more absorbing topic to a fellow-writer.

The short story is a form of fiction in which but few English have excelled, and none have reached the super-eminence of de Maupassant or of Anton Tchehov. It is a form in which, for perfection, an almost superhuman repression of the writer's self must go hand in hand with something that one can only describe as essence of writer—a something unmistakable but impalpable, and not to be laid finger on. In the perfect short story one is unconscious of anything but a fragrant trifle, so focused and painted before our minds, that it is as actual, and yet as rounded, as deep in colour, as fine in texture as a flower, and which withal disengages a perfume from—who knows where, that makes it a carnation not a rose, a Maupassant and not a Tchehov.

Now Cunninghame Graham sometimes—as in *Hegira*,

A Hatchment, and other stories—approaches this perfection.
I am not sure that he ever quite reaches it, for a reason
that, curiously, is his real strength as a writer. Very much
of an artist, he is yet too much of a personality ever to be
quite the pure artist; the individuality of the man will
thrust its spear-head through the stuff of his creations. I
may be wrong, but I cannot honestly recall any story of
his in which his knight-errant philosophy does not here and
there lift its head out of the fabric of his dreams, if not
directly, then through implicit contrast, or in choice of
subject. One can readily understand the queer potency
which this particular quality gives to his tales, in an age
and country very much surrendered to money and mate-
rialism. It is not that he is a romantic; on the contrary he
is a realist with a steel-keen eye, and a power of colouring
an exact picture hardly excelled. It is his clear, poignant
realism that makes his philosophy ring out so convinced and
convincing, and gives it the power to rip the gilding off the
shoddy and snobbishness of our civilisation.

The bent of his soul, and the travels of his body have
inclined him to those parts of the earth—the pampas, Mo-
rocco, Spain, Scotland—where there are still gleams at all
events of a life more primitive, more æsthetically attractive, and probably saner than our own; and when, as in *Un
Monsieur* and such studies as *Appreciation,* he pitches on a
purely 'civilised' setting, he rides home, indeed.

It is a rather strange thing, and a great tribute to his
personality, that throughout what is really a sustained attack
on certain habits of existence, and the bloated house they
have succeeded in building for themselves, he never once
gives the feeling of attacking for the sake of attacking.
The assault is delivered, as it were, not by his reason and
mind, but by his spirit and his nerves. As if, while he wrote,
the music of our high civilisation would keep intruding its
blusterous, rich, and flabby harmonies on his strange ears,

so that he must leap from his chair, and, sitting down again, die, or insert in his screed the word 'accursed.'

And the real beauty of him is that the things of which he writes that word, directly or by implication, in a hundred tales, are really mean and sordid in that true sense of a word which has not, as so many journalists appear to imagine, any connection with absence of income, or presence of human nature in back streets.

With his style I personally have sometimes a fault or two to find, but I recognise in it to the full those qualities of colour, vibration, and sense of the right word that alone keep life beating in a tale. Without high power of expression philosophy is of little use to any artist, weighting his pockets till he is sitting in the road instead of riding along it with his head up, as this writer always does. He has a manner, and a way with him, valuable at a time when certain leading writers have little or none at all. And he has a passion for the thing seen, that brings into his work the constant flash of revelation. He makes us see what he sees, and what he sees is not merely the surface.

Withal he is a gallant foe of oppression, of cruelty, of smugness, and fatty degeneration; a real tonic salt to the life of an age that needs it.

FOREWORD TO
'THE ASSEMBLED TALES OF STACY AUMONIER'

I write this Foreword with enthusiasm, for these are the assembled tales of a real master of the short story. The word 'great' has been so overdone, and the word 'genius' is so flyblown, that I shall use neither. Suffice it to say that Stacy Aumonier is one of the best short-story writers of all time, and that there is certainly no one more readable. And yet he, so untimely gone from us, has not yet attained the full eminence which is his due, and which I believe this volume will secure for him. It is for all and every; it will not date; it is gay reading, yet has the depth of a queer truth and wisdom. In it we find the cream of his literary output, for he was essentially a short-story writer rather than a novelist. I have re-read all the stories in this volume, and have been rejoiced and amazed, afresh, at the ease of the style, the richness and precision of the observation, the poignancy of the irony, and the humane breadth and tolerance of the feeling and philosophy. It is not an exaggeration to say that from first sentence to last my interest has never for a moment flagged. This was a temperament singularly fitted for the re-creation of life's little comedies and tragedies. The first essential in a short-story writer is the power of being interesting, sentence by sentence. Aumonier had this power in prime degree. You do not have to 'get into' his stories. He is especially notable for investing his figures with the breath of life within a few sentences. Take a short story like 'The Funny Man's Day'—how wonderfully well we know that funny man not as a type only but as a human being! How remarkably Miss Bracegirdle, in twenty minutes of our time, becomes a permanent acquaintance! How dreadfully intimate we get with the 'Two Friends!' That story, by the way, first of Aumonier's I ever read, first, I believe, ever published, was never surpassed by him for power, and sardonic grip on type and circumstance. It is as fine in its way as 'Boule de Suif,' and that is to say almost as much as can be said in praise of a short tale. There was, indeed, something Gallic in Aumonier's temperament, or at least in his talent—not in his style, which is very English, but in his way of envisaging his subjects. This is not remarkable, considering his name and his face; but in spite of his French look and his Huguenot origin, he was truly English in his humour and attitude to life. French in mind, he was English in heart; for no Frenchman——not even Monsieur André Maurois——could have conceived Alfred Codling——'the man of letters,' or 'the Great Unimpressionable,' or 'The Grayles,' or the waitress in 'Overboard,' or written 'The Match,' that perfect piece of English atmosphere.

A short-story writer is always beset by the temptation to be inventive rather than creative or even re-creative. This is a temptation to which Aumonier rarely if ever succumbed. He was profoundly in love with life, and impregnated through and through by curiosity about life and its manifestations, whether simple or queer. All types were fish to his net; and he has given us the fruits of his passion for and his curiosity about existence with a deft and always interesting fidelity. And with what sympathy he can hit off character! Take the 'Happy Man,' or the hero in 'Old Iron'——he feels and he can touch us with his feeling. He had faith, too, in the unbelievable, and he could make it real, as the unbelievable so often is in life. His humour is sly and dry and frequent and wholly delightful. And how he puts his finger on weak spots! Yet with what restraint he satirises!

Stacy Aumonier is never heavy, never boring, never really trivial; interested himself, he keeps us interested. At the back of his tales there is belief in life and a philosophy of life; of how many short-story writers can that be said? He understands the art of movement in a tale, he has the power of suggestion, he has a sense of line that most of us should envy; he is wholly uninfluenced by the dreary self-consciousness of novelty for novelty's sake. He is not tricky. He follows no fashion and no school. He is always himself. And can't he write! Ah! far better than far more pretentious writers. Nothing escapes his eye, but he describes without affectation or redundancy, and you sense in him a feeling for beauty that is never obtruded. He gets values right, and that is to say nearly everything. The easeful fidelity of his style has militated against his reputation in these somewhat posturing times. But his shade may rest in peace, for in this volume, at least, he will outlive nearly all the writers of his day.

PREFACE TO 'THE SPANISH FARM'

(R. H. MOTTRAM)

The Spanish Farm attracts a preface because it exhibits a new form, distinct even in this experimental epoch; and because one has not before met with such a good realisation of French character by an Englishman, unless René, in *Beauchamp's Career*, be excepted.

For four years and three months the British Army was in France, many thousands of educated Englishmen were in touch with French character, and, so far as I know, Madeleine in this book is the only full, solid, intimate piece of French characterisation which has resulted from that long and varied contact. Madeleine is amazingly lifelike. I suspect her to be a composite creation rather than drawn directly from one living prototype; however that may be, there she is, an individual Frenchwoman of the north, firm as ever stood on excellent legs—no compromise about her outlines, nothing fluffy and nothing sketchy in her portrait from beginning to end. She imposes herself, page by page, with tenacity, her clear knowledge of what she wants, her determined way of getting it, her quick blood, her business capacity, and once more, her tenacity—the tenacity which has kept the Spanish farm in her family since the days of Alva. Besides being a warm-blooded, efficient, decisive human being, with a wonderful eye to the main chance, she is evidence on French character extremely valuable to those among us who really want to understand the French.

And the minor portraits of her lover Georges, and his old parents, of her father, her sister, and the housekeeper at the château with the young English officer as foil, fill in a convincing picture of French life and atmosphere in the war zone.

I suppose you would call this a war book, but it is unlike any other war book that I, at least, have met with. Its defined and realised scope, its fidelity and entire freedom from meretricity, make it a singularly individual piece of work.

And that brings me to its form—the chief reason for this short preface. *The Spanish Farm* is not precisely a novel, and it is not altogether a chronicle; and here the interest comes in—quite clearly the author did not mean it to be a novel, and fail; nor did he mean it to be a chronicle, and fail. In other words, he was guided by mood and subject-matter into discovery of a new vehicle of expression—going straight ahead with that bold directness which guarantees originality. Easy enough to find fault with *The Spanish Farm* if you judge it strictly as a novel, or strictly as a chronicle, in fact if you take it strictly for what it is not— that pet weakness of hasty criticism. The book has its imperfections—what book has not?—but I do not think the serious critic can miss the peculiar unforced feeling of novelty its form has given me. You do not put it down saying: "I see perfectly what form the fellow was trying for, but he didn't bring it off." You put it down thinking: "The fellow didn't seem to be trying for any form, but he did bring it off."

We know the self-conscious chronicle in fiction, and its— as a rule—artificial effect. *The Spanish Farm* is as far from that as it is from the dramatic novel. It just goes its own way, and quietly defeats the search for parallels. One might perhaps best call it highly humanised history. It is, anyway, a very interesting book, with a just—if unexpected—title, for one never loses consciousness of

Madeleine's home, that solid farmstead of French Flanders, named in the Spanish wars of centuries ago, and still in being, after the greatest war of all time.

1924.

INTRODUCTION TO 'BLEAK HOUSE'
WAVERLEY EDITION (CHARLES DICKENS)

"Il péchait par l'excès de ses qualités. Il avait fait d'innombrables passions." So De Maupassant describes his earthy Colossus; so I am tempted to write of the spirit of Dickens. It certainly inspired a passion in me, the first serious and most abiding passion of my imaginative life. Reading this book again after twenty-seven years, I seem to remember nearly every word; not because this is my favourite Dickens—for I rate *The Pickwick Papers, David Copperfield, Our Mutual Friend* and *Martin Chuzzlewit* before it; but because I was in love with its author when I read it; because I read it—as I read every word of his, from the age of twelve to the age of seventeen—with passion. This has happened to me, I think, with only seven other novelists. With Whyte Melville—whose stoical dandies quite undermined my early constitution; with Thackeray, between the ages of seventeen and twenty-two; with Dumas *père*, who stole me from twenty-five to twenty-eight; with Turgenev, who possessed my mind and soul at about the age of thirty; with De Maupassant, who took his leavings; with Tolstoy, and in somewhat less degree, with Monsieur Anatole France. I never was a taster of books, a connoisseur, a dipper-in, a literary flirt; there had always to be in me a passion for the dish, or my appetite would have none of it. Outside the works of these seven novelists, I have had affairs with Mark Twain's *Tom Sawyer* and *Huckleberry Finn;* with *Don Quixote;* and with Flaubert's

Trois Contes. I am confessed. A singularly pure and blameless life, as literary lives do go.

What strikes me particularly, coming fresh again to this early love, is the utter readableness of it all. It remains untouched by all the literary water that has flowed since. There is, I suppose, within the covers of this book, no rule or canon of what we call æsthetics that is not forty times violated. There is neither line nor shape; neither coherent inevitability, nor moral discovery. The plot is coincidental and melodramatic; the characters for the most part caricatures. Moralising stalks unashamed, the humour is often blatant, and the pathos has been dipped in treacle. The style has no peculiar grace. All the little gods of art blush all over their little faces at every other page. And yet——! The sheer fecundity of it; the sheer vitality; the sweep and range; the compelling, strange, haphazard felicity! Ah! my little gods of art, we could do with a bit more of these where you hold sway. It is genius indeed that can rise so superior to its own technique. In truth, the big mind, the splendid sympathy of the man Dickens makes his work to-day as living as it was in those days when—we knew no better! Search these pages, you will find nothing that does not come out of a fine and generous heart, a heart that hated meanness, and hated cruelty—those twin and only real vices of mankind; and you will find nothing that, however queerly said, was not worth saying. The instinctive wisdom of it all; the marvellous way in which the finger of the writer's mood traverses the trappings and the wrappings, and finds the true pulsation and heart-beat of things!

Though by the pen of Dickens England was created—an England more living, on the whole, than the real article—it sometimes seems to me that there never was an English writer so un-English. That dryness in our blood and bones, which comes of a wet climate; our thin and cranky stiffness; our horrid terror of neighbours' eyes—he had them not. He was in flux; a volcano ever active; and the mountains he threw up had more variety of shape than all the hills of all our other writers of fiction put together.

Yes, Dickens had the finest unrestraint of any Englishman ever begotten; and what distinguishes him from every other English novelist was the strange mingling in his nature of interest in the bizarre and abnormal, with comprehension of the main types of human character. That the extraordinary Krooks and Miss Flites of this life should flow with the same zest from his brain as the Mrs. Jellabys, the Skimpoles, the Tulkinghorns, and Richard Carstones, who represent, each in their way, a main line of human weakness, is terrific tribute to his scope. That he was always less successful with his angelic conceptions is only to say that the heroic is a theme for poetry, and not for prose. The novelist who looks up to his characters can never make them live. Jarndyce and Esther Summerson are but the less vital by reason of the upward eye that Dickens cast on them; he dared not touch them with the comic, and their blood lacks the red corpuscles that characters imbibe in the grosser atmospheres of their creator's mind. The simple heroism of Caddy, Prince Turveydrop, and Lawrence Boythorn shines out like gold, because they are envisaged by the steady and full-fronting eye of one not forcing on them his own aspirations. They have no wings, and for that are the nearer to heaven. Is "the beautiful character" —so generally female—ever convincing? I do not think I know of one in the whole range of fiction. Perhaps, one should rather phrase it thus: Is there a single character in all fiction, who rivets and enchants us, unless his or her foibles, as well as virtues, have been seen and painted? I have yet to find that extraordinary fowl. The presentation of heroism is a too subtle thing to be achieved by the frontal attack—its glow is soon damped-down by worship. It must

capture you unawares by fugitive gleams; it must peer at
you mysteriously from out of the clay. Dickens occasionally
went for it bald-headed. Well! When he did, he failed.
But he was no great sinner in that respect. His failures,
Esther Summerson, Agnes Wickfield, Florence Dombey,
Kate Nickleby, his Jarndyce, and Nicholas Nickleby, are
but a fraction of the mighty sum of his creatures, though
he sailed rather near the wind, too, with such as Tom
Pinch, and Mark Tapley, and even Tommy Traddles. *Il
péchait par l'excès de ses qualités*—when he saw good he
saw sugar-good, and when he saw evil black was no word
for his ink.

We poor novelists who in these æsthetic days are nearly
banned for expressing our temperamental hatreds, what
fools we are to Dickens! His sword was drawn indeed, he
passed it through and through all God-forsaken things;
and who now has a stone to cast at him for his long cru-
sade against all shams, and cruel stupidities? But what a
sword!

" 'Why! bless my heart!' says Mr. Snagsby, 'what's the
matter?'

" 'This boy,' says the constable, 'although he's repeatedly
told to, won't move on——'

" 'I'm always a-moving on, sir!' cries the boy, wiping
away his grimy tears with his arm. 'I've always been a-moving and a-moving on, ever since I was born. Where can I
possibly move to, sir, more nor I do move?'

" 'He won't move on,' says the constable calmly . . . 'although he's been repeatedly cautioned, and therefore I am
obliged to take him into custody. He's as obstinate a young
gonoph as I know. He WON'T move on.'

" 'O my eye! Where can I move to?' cries the boy,
clutching quite desperately at his hair, and beating his bare
feet upon the floor of Mr. Snagsby's passage.

" 'Don't you come none of that, or I shall make blessed

short work of you!' says the constable, giving him a passion-less shake. 'My instructions are, that you are to move on. I have told you so five hundred times.'

" 'But where?' cries the boy.

" 'Well! Really, constable, you know,' says Mr. Snagsby wistfully, and coughing behind his hand his cough of great perplexity and doubt; 'really that does seem a question. Where, you know?'

" 'My instructions don't go to that,' replies the constable. 'My instructions are that this boy is to move on.' "

This is noble satire, and fine art—though all the little gods blush at the very next paragraph, in which the author presents us with the same sentiment divested of all clothing. *Il péchait*——! No matter! He riddled Bumbledom, as no one before or since has riddled it. He riddled departmental idiocy, till the wind of a wider, sweeter world whistled through its holes, and blew a gale inside.

When I was a boy, reading him with passion, I but vaguely glimpsed his glorious tourney; now that I know the world a little and have seen God's own Bumbles, I never tire of standing by the roadside with a humble hat in hand, to see his gallant and great spirit ride past.

1912.

PREFACE TO 'ANNA KARENINA'

CENTENARY EDITION (LEO TOLSTOY)

TOLSTOY is a fascinating puzzle. So singular an instance of artist and reformer rolled into one frame is not, I think, elsewhere to be found. The preacher in him, who took such charge of his later years, was already casting a shadow over the artist-writer of *Anna Karenina*. There is even an

indication of the moralist in the last part of that tremendous novel: *War and Peace*. About his work, in fact,
is an ever-present sense of spiritual duality. It is a battle-
field on which we watch the ebb and flow of unending
conflict, the throb and stress of a gigantic disharmony. Ex-
planation of this mysterious duality must be left to the
doctors, now that our personalities are controlled by our
glands, so that if we have plenty of pituitary we are artists,
and too little adrenal—is it?—moralists.

In choosing a single novel to label with those words so
dear to the confectioners of symposiums, 'The greatest ever
written,' I would select *War and Peace*. In it Tolstoy
rides two themes, like a circus-rider on his two piebald
horses, and by a miracle reaches the stable door still
mounted and still whole. The secret of his triumph lies in
the sheer interest with which his creative energy has in-
vested every passage. The book is six times as long as an
ordinary novel, but it never flags, never wearies the reader;
and the ground—of human interest and historical event,
of social life and national life—covered in it, is prodigious.
A little, but not much, behind that masterwork, comes
Anna Karenina. Also of stupendous length, this novel con-
tains, in the old prince, in his daughter Kitty, in Stepan
Arkadyevich, Vronsky, Levin, and Anna herself, six of
Tolstoy's most striking characters. He never drew a better
portrait than that of Stepan Arkadyevich—the perfect
Russian man of the world; the writer of this preface has
known the very spit of him. The opening chapters, describing him at an unkind moment in his fortunes, are
inimitable. As for the portrait of Anna's husband, Alexey
Alexandrovich—it inspires in us the feelings that he must
have inspired in Anna. The early parts of this great novel
are the best, for I have never been convinced that Anna,
in the circumstances shown, would have committed suicide.
It is as if Tolstoy had drawn her for us with such colour

and solidity in the beginning, that we cannot believe she is not in the end dismissed by him rather than by herself. Anna, in fact, is a warm pulsating person, with too much vitality to go out as she did. The finish strikes one as *voulu*, as if the creator had turned against his creature; and one forms the opinion that Tolstoy started on this book with the free hand of an unlimited sympathy and understanding, but during the years that passed before he finished it, became subtly changed in his outlook over life, and ended in fact a preacher who had set out as an artist. It is, however, no uncommon flaw in writers to misjudge the vitality of their own creations. An illustration of the same defect is the suicide of Paula in *The Second Mrs. Tanqueray*. Ladies with her sort of past have too much vitality to put a period to themselves, except in plays and novels. With this reservation *Anna Karenina* is a great study of Russian character, and a great picture of Russian society—a picture that held good, with minor variations, up to the war.

Tolstoy's method in this novel, as in all his work, is cumulative—the method of an infinity of facts and pictorial detail; the opposite of Turgenev's, who relied on selection and concentration, on atmosphere and poetic balance. Tolstoy fills in all the spaces, and leaves little to the imagination; but with such vigour, such freshness, that it is all interesting. His style, in the narrow sense, is by no means remarkable. All his work bears the impress of a mind more concerned with the thing said than with the way to say it. But if one may add to interminable definitions: 'Style is the power in a writer to remove all barriers between himself and his reader—the triumph of style is the creation of intimacy;' then, though such a definition will put many out of court, it will leave Tolstoy a stylist; for no author, in his story-telling, produces a more intimate feeling of actual life. He is free, in fact, from the literary self-consciousness which so often spoils the work of polished writers. Tolstoy was carried away by his impulses, whether creative or reformative. He never stood on the shores of streams, trying first one foot and then the other—that pet vice of modern art. To have life and meaning, art must emanate from one *possessed by his theme*. The rest of art is just exercise in technique, which helps artists to render the greater impulses when—too seldom—they come. As with the painter who spends half his life agonising over what he ought to be—Post-Impressionist, Cubist, Futurist, Expressionist, Dadaist, Paulo-Post-Dadaist (or whatever they are by now)—who is ever developing a new and wonderful technique and changing his æsthetic outlook, and whose work, like his mood, is self-conscious and tentative, so with the writer. Only when a theme seizes on him is all doubt about expression resolved, and a masterwork produced.

The prime characteristic of Tolstoy as a novelist was certainly his unflinching sincerity, his resolute exposition of what seemed to him the truth at the moment. Remembering how he swung between the artist and the moralist, we have in that trait at once his strength and his weakness. Frankly loyal, true to the vision and mood of the moment, he had a force that philosophic reflection lacks, together with its corollary—deficient balance. His native force is proved by the simple fact that, taking up again one of his stories after the lapse of many years, one will remember almost every paragraph. Dickens and Dumas are perhaps the only other writers who compare with him in this respect.

The character of Levin is undoubtedly a *Selbst-Porträt*, or at least a study of the side of Tolstoy's own nature which was preoccupying him at that period. The chapters describing Levin in the country are very clearly a rendering of his own efforts and feelings, just when he was beginning to be profoundly disturbed about the meaning of life, and to develop his 'peasant' philosophy of existence. And in this part of the novel we again have a feeling of earnest message at the back of portraiture. The whole of Tolstoy's writing life, indeed, after this novel, is very much of an effort to prove that what he himself felt and saw was what the average man could feel and see. And in all this long attempt we are conscious of the distortion which comes when an artist and thinker tries to put himself into the skin of the normal man, or rather, tries to put the normal man into his own skin. A useful illustration of such distortion occurs in one of Conrad's early stories—*The Return*—where a notably matter-of-fact English husband agonises over his wife's departure, in Slavonic fashion, during many long and intricate pages. In the light shed by history and more recent analysts we must be permitted to doubt whether Tolstoy really understood the Russian peasant, whom he elevated into a sort of arbiter of life and art. Perhaps he understood them as well as an aristocrat could; but he is not so close to the soul and body of Russia as Tchehov, who came of the people and knew them from inside. In any case, the Russia of Tolstoy's great novels: *War and Peace* and *Anna Karenina,* is a Russia of the past, perhaps only the crust of that Russia of the past—now split and crumbled beyond repair. How fortunate we are, then, to have two such supreme pictures of the vanished fabric!

1926.

THE GREAT TREE

WHEN the human spirit, joyful or disconsolate, seeks perch for its happy feet, or stay for flagging wings, it comes back again and again to the great tree of Shakespeare's genius, whose evergreen no heat withers, no cold blights, whose security no wind can loosen.

Rooted in the good brown soil, sunlight or the starshine

on its leaves, this great tree stands, a refuge and home for the spirits of men.

Why are the writings of Shakespeare such an everlasting solace and inspiration?

Because, in an incomprehensible world, full of the savage and the stupid and the suffering, stocked with monstrous contrasts and the most queer happenings, they do not fly to another world for compensation. They are of Earth and not of Heaven. They blink nothing, dare everything, but even in tragedy, never lose their sane unconscious rapture, and prepossession with that entrancing occupation which we call 'life.' Firm in reality, they embody the faith that sufficient unto this Earth is the beauty and the meaning thereof. Theirs is, as it were, the proud exuberance of Nature, and no eye turned on the hereafter; and so thy fill us with gladness to be alive—though 'the rain it raineth every day.'

Truth condescended for a moment when Shakespeare lived, withdrew her bandage and looked out; and good and evil, beauty and distortion, laughter and gloom for once were mirrored as they are, beneath this sun and moon.

What a wide, free, careless spirit was this man Shakespeare's—incarnate lesson to narrow-headed mortals, their strait moralities, and pedantic hearts! And what a Song he sang; clothing Beauty for all time in actuality, in strangeness, and variety!

'He wanted arte,' Ben Jonson said; 'I would he had blotted a thousand lines!' No doubt! And yet, Ben Jonson: What is art?

In every tree, even the greatest, dead wood and leaves shrivelled from birth, abound; but never was a spirit-tree where the rich sap ran up more freely, never a tree whose height and circumference were greater, whose leaves so glistened; where astonished Spring fluttered such green buds; breezes made happier sound in Summer, whispering;

the Autumn gales a deeper roaring; nor, in Winter, reigned so rare a silent beauty of snow.

In this Great Tree, I think there shall never be, in the time of man:

"Bare ruin'd choirs, where late the sweet birds sang."
(Sonnet LXXIII).

1915.

FOUR DRAMATIC PIECES

THE WINTER GARDEN

A Symphonic Squib

CHARACTERS

Sir George Blane	. G.C.B.
Lady Blane .	. His Wife
Miss Blane . .	. His Daughter
Captain Blane .	. D.S.O.
Canon Bath .	. A Valetudinarian
Rev. Handel Mildred	A Sleepless Chaplain
Mr. Kenealy .	. A Scotsman
Mr. Fitch . .	. A Silent Solicitor
Mrs. Fitch . .	. His Nervous Wife
Mrs. Campion .	. A Wandering Widow
Mrs. Bird . .	. A Detached Woman
The Honourable	
Gertrude Sloaney .	A Traveller for Health
Monsieur Vert .	. The Hotel Proprietor

THE WINTER GARDEN

Before the curtain rises a hum of noises is heard, ending with a violent sneeze. LADY BLANE's *voice rises.*

LADY BLANE:
  Did you get your game, George?

SIR GEORGE:
  What?

There is the sound of another loud shrill sneeze; it is repeated. The curtain rises on CANON BATH's *third sneeze.*

The scene disclosed is the Winter Garden of a Riviera hotel in January, greenly caparisoned with plants, chairs, rugs, divans, and heated with hot air. MR. *and* MRS. FITCH *are playing chess.*

LADY BLANE:
  Did you get your game, George?

SIR GEORGE:
  What? Yes.

MISS BLAINE:
  Did you win, Dad?

SIR GEORGE:
  Yes. What?

CANON BATH sneezes.

HON. GERTRUDE [*sotto voce*]:
  That poor old gentleman—it's *rather*——

SIR GEORGE:
  What?

LADY BLANE:
  Quite!

MR. KENEALY *loudly crackles "The Times," and looks round it over his spectacles. His face is fresh-coloured and bearded, with shrewd eyes.*

MRS. BIRD [*in a soft, sympathetic voice*]:
I'm always so sorry for people who read *The Times;* such a very loud noise——

CAPTAIN BLANE:
Ye-e-e-as!

MRS. BIRD:
Don't you think?

CAPTAIN BLANE:
Ye-e-e-as!

CANON BATH *sneezes. All look at him.* MRS. CAMPION *rests her knitting and sniffs.*

HON. GERTRUDE:
I do think it's *rather*——

LADY BLANE:
Quite!

MRS. FITCH *titters.*

REV. HANDEL:
Er—I tried bromide last night—er——

MISS BLANE:
Oh! Mr. Mildred, do tell me the effect. [*Whooping*] It's got such a *funny* taste.

REV. HANDEL:
It—er——

SIR GEORGE:
What?

CANON BATH *sneezes. The* REV. HANDEL *does not finish his remark.* MRS. BIRD *is talking in a cooing manner to* CAPTAIN BLANE.

CAPTAIN BLANE:
Ye-e-e-as! Ye-e-e-as! She's lookin' very seedy; quite pulled down.

MRS. BIRD [*cooing*]:
Um!

CAPTAIN BLANE:
Ye-e-e-as!

LADY BLANE:
How many holes up were you, George?

SIR GEORGE:
What?

MR. KENEALY *crackles "The Times" and looks round it.* MR. FITCH *clears his throat sonorously.*

LADY BLANE:
How many holes up were you, George?

SIR GEORGE:
Three. What?

HON. GERTRUDE:
Oh! That's *rather*——

LADY BLANE:
Quite!

CAPTAIN BLANE [*in answer to* MRS. BIRD]:
Ye-e-e-as!

MRS. CAMPION *sniffs.*

REV. HANDEL:
I'm going——er——to try sulphonal to-night.

HON. GERTRUDE:
That's *rather* daring.

LADY BLANE:
Quite.

SIR GEORGE:
  What?

MISS BLANE:
  Mr. Millicent says he's going to try [*whooping*] *sulphonal* to-night.

SIR GEORGE:
  What?

REV. HANDEL:
  Sulphonal, Sir George; they say it makes you go off——

  CANON BATH *sneezes.*

REV. HANDEL:
  Beautifully.

SIR GEORGE:
  Sulphonal?

LADY BLANE:
  Quite! I've tried it.

SIR GEORGE:
  What?

MISS BLANE [*whooping*]:
  Mother says she's tried it.

  MR. KENEALY *crackles "The Times."*

CAPTAIN BLANE [*in answer to* MRS. BIRD]:
  Ye-e-e-as. Had a lot of trouble with his horses. He's a good sort; ye-e-e-as!

MRS. BIRD [*cooing*]:
  Umm!

CAPTAIN BLANE:
  Ye-e-e-as!

  MR. FITCH *clears his throat.*

REV. HANDEL:
To-morrow night, if sulphonal doesn't operate, I shall
—er—try putting my feet in cold water.

MISS BLANE:
Oh! Mr. Mildred, how *beastly* for them in the middle
of the night!

SIR GEORGE [*interested*]:
What?

    CANON BATH *sneezes.*

HON. GERTRUDE:
Mr. Mildred says he's going to try cold water; it seems
rather——

LADY BLANE:
Quite! Are you going to play to-morrow?

SIR GEORGE:
If I can get anyone to come out.

REV. HANDEL:
I'd play with you, General, if—er——

HON. GERTRUDE [*sotto voce to him*]:
Oh! That's rather good of you!

SIR GEORGE:
What?

MISS BLANE:
Mr. Mildred says [*whoops*] he'd play with you if——

    CANON BATH *sneezes.*

SIR GEORGE [*rubbing his hands*]:
I'll take him on.

LADY BLANE:
He can't sleep.

SIR GEORGE:
Sleep? Who wants to sleep—what?

MR. FITCH:
Check. [*He clears his throat.*]

    MRS. FITCH *titters.* MRS. CAMPION *looks at them and sniffs.*

CAPTAIN BLANE [*in answer to* MRS. BIRD]:
Ye-e-e-as, it would; ye-e-e-as. What do you say, Canon Bath?

CANON BATH [*sneezing*]:
The climate here is indifferent; too easterly, too dry-ing——

MRS. BIRD:
Umm, umm!

CANON BATH:
Too localised.

CAPTAIN BLANE:
Ye-e-e-as.

    CANON BATH *sneezes.*

REV. HANDEL:
I've tried hay-flower baths, Lady Blane—they were——

HON. GERTRUDE:
Oh! They're *rather*——

MISS BLANE:
They're so [*whoops*] *beastly* messy.

REV. HANDEL:
Er—do you know Cannes, Lady Blane?

LADY BLANE:
Quite!

REV. HANDEL:
Er—I didn't sleep in Cannes——

    MR. KENEALY *crackles* "*The Times.*" MRS. CAMPION *gets up, sniffs, and sits down again.*

SIR GEORGE:
What?

LADY BLANE:
Will you have your tea, George?

REV. HANDEL:
Tea keeps me awake all night.

CAPTAIN BLANE [*to* MRS. BIRD]:
Ye-e-e-as. Nice little woman. Ye-e-e-as. Goes there for her health.

MRS. BIRD [*cooing*]:
Umm, umm!

CAPTAIN BLANE:
Ye-e-e-as. Awf'lly poor health.

MRS. BIRD:
Umm!

CAPTAIN BLANE:
Ye-e-e-as!

CANON BATH:
You were speaking of her health. [*He sneezes.*]

MRS. CAMPION *again gets up, sniffs, and again sits down. As she resumes her seat,* MR. KENEALY *crackles "The Times" with desperation. There is a silence.*

SIR GEORGE [*suddenly*]:
Never was in such a dull place in my life. What?

MISS BLANE:
I'll go and see if the glass is going up.

She rises, crosses left, and goes out under an arch left forward. CANON BATH *sneezes.*

SIR GEORGE:
What?

MRS. BIRD [*raising her voice*]:
I do think it's so delicious there, don't you, Canon Bath?

CANON BATH:
There is a prevalence of north wind.

MRS. BIRD:
Umm!

CANON BATH:
The aspect—— [*He sneezes.*]

CAPTAIN BLANE:
Ye-e-e-as!

SIR GEORGE [*suddenly*]:
Will you take me on at chess, Miss Sloaney? What?

HON. GERTRUDE:
I'm rather afraid——

MR. FITCH:
Check. [*He clears his throat.* MRS. FITCH *titters.*]

SIR GEORGE [*with a disgusted movement*]:
Those people have got the men. They've always got 'em.
What?

LADY BLANE:
Your tea's gettin' cold, George. Quite! [*Re-enter* MISS
BLANE, *pleasurably excited. She is followed in a few seconds by* MONSIEUR VERT, *the hotel proprietor, a short
square man with a short square beard.*]

MISS BLANE [*whooping*]:
The hotel bus has upset.

SIR GEORGE:
What?

MISS BLANE:
The hotel bus has [*whooping*] upset!

There are signs of great animation in the Winter

*Garden, all rising instinctively.   Mr. and Mrs. Fitch,
recollecting that they do not know the Blanes, resume
their seats in eager but suspended animation; Mrs.
Campion remains standing and still knitting, with her
eyes fixed on the group right, which now includes
Captain Blane, Mrs. Bird, and outlying portions of
the seated Canon Bath.   Mr. Kenealy regards them
above "The Times."*

Lady Blane:
Here's Monsieur Vert! Tell me, please. [Monsieur
Vert *approaches*.]   How did it happen?

Hon. Gertrude [*concerned*]:
It's *rather* dreadful!

Captain Blane:
I say, look here, can I do anything—the horses!

Mrs. Bird:
Oh! The *poor* horses!

Canon Bath:
Has anybody suffered injury?

   Monsieur Vert *is about to reply.*

Sir George:
Who was drivin' the d——d thing? Drunk, I suppose!
What?

Rev. Handel:
Er—was he badly——?

Sir George:
What?

Mrs. Bird:
Poor man!

Lady Blane:
Is he *quite*——

MONSIEUR VERT [*speaking for the first time*]:
It is—nodings—it is a she——

SIR GEORGE:
What?

MRS. CAMPION [*approaching resolutely, disregarding or perhaps remembering the fact that she is not yet within the circle of the Blanes' acquaintance, and producing smelling salts*]:
These are very strong.

MONSIEUR VERT:
It was a she——

    CANON BATH *rises with a sneeze.*

SIR GEORGE:
The devil! I can't hear. What?

MONSIEUR VERT:
A lady of the town——

SIR GEORGE:
What?

    There is a considerable decrescendo of interest.

LADY BLANE:
Monsieur Vert says a lady of the town was hurt.

SIR GEORGE:
Where? What?

MRS. BIRD [*languidly*]:
Poor thing!

CANON BATH:
Very careless. [*He resumes his seat.*]

MONSIEUR VERT [*with some excitement*]:
No, no; it was nod. It was a she-dog—a beech——

    CANON BATH *sneezes.*

SIR GEORGE:
   What?

MONSIEUR VERT:
   Her leetle dog bit her behind——de leg.

CAPTAIN BLANE:
   Really? Ha, he! Ha, ha!

SIR GEORGE [*brightening*]:
   Leg? What?

MRS. CAMPION [*to* SIR GEORGE, *taking charge of the
      incident*]:
   The bus upset, and a Frenchwoman's little dog who was
seated in it bit her by the leg.

LADY BLANE [*frigidly*]:
   Quite! George, will you have some fresh tea?

   MRS. CAMPION, *with an angry look at* LADY BLANE,
sniffs and retires towards the settee.

HON. GERTRUDE:
   The poor little dog. It's *rather* hard on it.

MISS BLANE:
   Poor darling! I'm sure she frightened it by *squealing*.
[*She whoops.*]

CAPTAIN BLANE:
   My French fencin' master's dog once saw him fightin',
and took him by the trousers.

HON. GERTRUDE:
   Not really!

CAPTAIN BLANE:
   Tore them! Ye-e-e-as!

MRS. BIRD:
   Umm!

CAPTAIN BLANE:
Ye-e-e-as!

LADY BLANE [*abruptly*]:
Did the silly woman ill-treat the dog after it bit her,
Monsieur Vert?

MONSIEUR VERT [*a little surprised*]:
She is blooded!

SIR GEORGE:
What?

LADY BLANE:
Monsieur Vert says the woman bled.

SIR GEORGE:
Best thing in the world for her. What?

HON. GERTRUDE:
But the poor little dog——?

MISS BLANE:
Where is it?

MONSIEUR VERT:
It's deeth are sharp. It ees here somewhere.

LADY BLANE [*decidedly*]:
Frightened out of its wits—poor little thing!

MISS BLANE:
I *must* look after it. [*She runs off left, followed by*
MONSIEUR VERT.]

CANON BATH:
I do not care for foreign dogs. [*He sneezes.*]

   MR. KENEALY *rattles "The Times" angrily, as
though to ask for silence.*

SIR GEORGE [*muttering*]:
What an infernal noise!

At this moment a spirited black Toy Pomeranian enters from left, followed by MISS BLANE.

HON. GERTRUDE:
It's *rather* a darling!

CAPTAIN BLANE:
Jolly little beggar——ye-e-e-as!

MRS. BIRD:
Sweet!

LADY BLANE:
Quite!

MRS. CAMPION *sniffs. There is a movement towards the dog, which is captured. They surround the dog, and stare at it.*

MISS BLANE:
It's hungry.

CANON BATH:
Don't put it near *my* legs, please.

MISS BLANE:
It wouldn't hurt a fly. Would you, *darling?* [*She kisses its nose.*]

Re-enter MONSIEUR VERT *from left.*

MONSIEUR VERT:
De lady wishes her leedle daug.

There is a silence, marked by resentment on the ladies' faces.

LADY BLANE [*decisively*]:
Has she got over her hysteria?

MISS BLANE [*whooping*]:
Oh! Not yet! I want to *feed* it. Can't you say it's run away?

HON. GERTRUDE [*with a smile*]:
That's *rather* daring!

LADY BLANE:
Will you guarantee that she won't ill-use it, Monsieur Vert?

SIR GEORGE:
Let him have the tyke! What?

MISS BLANE:
Father!

MONSIEUR VERT:
De lady——

CAPTAIN BLANE:
Look here——is it a bad bite? I know something **about** bites.

MONSIEUR VERT:
She haf nod showed me; it is close by de knee. [MRS. CAMPION *sniffs.*]

CAPTAIN BLANE [*smoothing his moustaches*]:
I see——ye-e-e-as!

LADY BLANE:
Silly woman!

MONSIEUR VERT:
I will take de daug, plese.

CANON BATH:
It will be better to allow Monsieur to take the dog.

REV. HANDEL:
Er——I think——perhaps——

MISS BLANE:
Oh! but——Mr. Mildred, if she [*whooping*] *beats* it——

HON. GERTRUDE:
That would be *rather* dreadful!

MONSIEUR VERT:
Plese to let me haf de daug, Mees.

MRS. CAMPION [*coming resolutely forward*]:
I will take the dog to her, and see that she does not ill-treat it.

> LADY *and* MISS BLANE, *the* HON. GERTRUDE *and* MRS. BIRD *gaze at her with incipient toleration. With a look round of bland ingratiation* MRS. CAMPION *takes the dog from* MISS BLANE *and proceeds left, followed by* MONSIEUR VERT.

LADY BLANE:
Quite!

HON. GERTRUDE:
It's *rather* sweet of her!

CAPTAIN BLANE:
Ye-e-e-as!

MISS BLANE:
I must go too.

> *She,* CAPTAIN BLANE, *and* MRS. BIRD *follow in a line. The remaining occupants of the Winter Garden sink back into the precise attitudes they occupied at the opening of the scene. There is a silence of some seconds.*

SIR GEORGE:
Never was in such a dog-hole in my life!

LADY BLANE:
Will you have some fresh tea, George? This is cold—quite.

SIR GEORGE:
What? [*There is another silence.*]

REV. HANDEL [*sidling towards* LADY BLANE *on the divan*]:
Er—I'm very much afraid—that I shan't sleep to-night, after this—er——

> *As he reaches the word* "to-night" *re-enter quickly*

Miss Blane, Mrs. Campion, Mrs. Bird, *and* Captain Blane *in a line. And*

Simultaneously

Hon. Gertrude:
That's *rather*——

Lady Blane:
Quite!

Miss Blane [*beginning with a whoop*]:
I say——

Captain Blane [*in answer to a sentence of* Mrs. Bird's]:
Ye-e-e-as!

Mrs. Bird:
Ummm!

Mrs. Campion *sniffs.*

Sir George [*Who has nodded off, with tremendous vehemence*]:
What?

Canon Bath *discharges an enormous sneeze.*
Mr. Fitch *clears his throat with special loudness.*
Mrs. Fitch *titters shrilly.*
Mr. Kenealy *hits "The Times" a fearful blow, which makes it crackle to the soul.*
Suddenly, as if startled by this chord of sound, all are silent, and look at each other.

The Curtain *falls.*

Circa 1908.

ESCAPE

EPISODE VII
THE FOXHUNTER

ESCAPE

An hour passed. A road on the edge of the moor. MATT, *who has been kneeling by his car, which has broken down, raises himself to see the figure of a dismounted* FOXHUNTER *coming towards him.*

FOXHUNTER:

Engine trouble? [MATT *nods.*] Well, she hasn't got away from you, like my beast. Come across a mare loose?

MATT:

Afraid not.

FOXHUNTER:

Never rains but it pours. Positively first car I've met, and lo! she's in trouble.

MATT [*taking in the* FOXHUNTER, *who is obviously a young man of his own species*]:

Seen the convict, Sir?

FOXHUNTER:

No; but they've all been keeping their eyes peeled.

MATT:

Aha! So have I.

FOXHUNTER [*with some distaste*]:

Not a pastime I care for——shan't view-halloa if *I* see him.

MATT:

Why not? Can't have desperadoes loose on the moor. Safety first!

FOXHUNTER:

But this poor devil's a gentleman.

MATT:

Nothing like a gentleman for being unsafe.

233

FOXHUNTER [*with increasing displeasure*]:
What! Poor draggled brute with the whole pack at his heels—dangerous!

MATT [*grinning*]:
Fox at bay!

FOXHUNTER:
Fox we killed to-day was digested in two minutes by my watch.

MATT:
Have hounds gone home?

FOXHUNTER:
Yes; they went on over. Mare unshipped me at the edge of a bog—went in plump, and got away while I was collecting myself.

MATT [*eyeing mudstains*]:
I see. Well, I'd change places with you. [*Gazing at car*] This is the least attractive Ford I ever drove.

FOXHUNTER:
Your own?

MATT:
No; belongs to some friends. They said I might take a run on the moor and look for the convict.

FOXHUNTER:
Good for the convict! Been fishing too?

MATT:
No. Camouflage.

FOXHUNTER [*with increasing displeasure*]:
Gosh! You really are out man-hunting?

MATT:
I say—*you're* not the convict, by any chance?

FOXHUNTER:

I? What the———? My good Sir, should I tell you, if I were?

MATT:

M'm, no! Forgive my asking. But they always change their clothes first thing, and yours are so priceless. You could get out of Abraham's bosom in that rig.

FOXHUNTER [*eyeing* MATT *with suspicion*]:

Look here! What made you ask that damn fool question?

MATT:

Well—your sympathy with him. You're about his size and appearance too, judging from the papers. And a soldier-man into the bargain, if I'm any judge.

FOXHUNTER [*hastily*]:

Quite right! And that's why I dislike a fellow-soldier being harried by seedy-looking blokes in Ford flivvers.

MATT [*goggling*]:

Masterly description; got me where I live, as the Yanks say. Still, a foxhunter's togs are as good as a passport any day, and you've got 'em on.

FOXHUNTER [*dangerously*]:

Are you looney? Or merely trying to be funny?

MATT [*suddenly serious*]:

Do you really want that convict chap to get off?

FOXHUNTER:

What's your game, my friend? [*Staring hard*] Are you a 'tec?

MATT:

No. [*Slowly*] I'm the convict. Change clothes with me! In your togs I could get through.

FOXHUNTER [*completely taken aback*]:
   I say! But—but——

MATT [*with a sad little smile*]:
   It's all right. I *am* the convict, but I was only kidding
you about the change. Thanks for your sympathy though.
You don't know what it means. You'd better get on now.
I'm going to take cover again.

FOXHUNTER [*uncertainly—looking from his garments to*
      MATT]:
   But look here—if you mean that you really——

MATT:
   No, no! Too thick! Accessory and all that. If you
could drive that flivver away, though, you'd do me a good
turn. But you can't, I'm afraid; she's bust her vitals.
Well, I must do my bunk now. Hope you'll catch your
mare. You might say you saw someone like me going up
that way.

FOXHUNTER:
   You've winded me; I don't know what to say—it's a
knock-out. Well, anyway, you can rely on me.

MATT:
   I know. Sojer to sojer! So long! [*He vanishes.*]

FOXHUNTER [*to himself*]:
   Gee-hovah! That's a rum go!

1926.

THE GOLDEN EGGS

FROM AN UNFINISHED PLAY

THE GOLDEN EGGS

ACT I

*In his comfortable study, which looks out over the Regent's
Park,* AUGUSTUS FREVILLE (*Gus*), *well-groomed, and
perhaps fifty, is divided between the desire to smoke his
morning cigar, and the feeling that anything so nice is
inappropriate to his frequently remembered anxiety. He
fidgets from the open window to the closed door of the
drawing-room, where the specialist is interviewing "poor
Blanche." He takes the cigar from a box on a table
well-stocked with papers and periodicals, and nicks it
absent-mindedly. Really! This is an intolerable business
—this dreadful weakness of poor dear Blanche—intolerably anxious—quite intolerably! And a beautiful
morning—delightfully sunny! Everything coming out
in the Park. The lilac! Ah! Delicious! He interrupts
his sniff to listen, and murmurs to himself:*

FREVILLE:

Intolerable—this waiting! Poor Blanche!

*He drums his fingers on the table, and the matches
catch his eye. He strikes one, and lo!—the cigar is
lighted! Delicious first draw! Delicious! A sound—he
puts the cigar behind his back, recoiling to the window,
whence a gesture will dispose of it. Nothing! He
smokes. The birds! The spring birds—delightful! He
murmurs:*

Jolly little beggars! That thrush! Delicious! Tt—tt!
Poor Blanche! Damn that doctor—why doesn't he come
out? [*He takes a letter from his pocket and quizzically
regards it; brushes back his fair grizzled hair compla-
cently.*] Poor Flo! [*Begins whistling "When the heart of
a man," but, suddenly remembering that he is very anxious,
looks at the drawing-room door, ceases to whistle, and sighs*

heavily.] This is really—— [*Abruptly he puts his cigar into his mouth, and the letter back into his pocket; advances half way to the drawing-room door, suddenly sees it opening, and stops—his face long, and his cigar behind him, the picture of perfectly sincere apprehension.*] Well, doctor?

The specialist—grey, clean-shaved, rather bald, with pince-nez, and a docketing eye, has turned to close the door; FREVILLE, *about to throw the cigar out of the window, has not quite time.*

DOCTOR [*advancing from the door*]:
My dear Mr. Freville—the poor dear lady is most plucky—most plucky.

FREVILLE:
I know, I know. But *how* is she?

DOCTOR:
So plucky that it's difficult to get anything from her, but [*he shakes his head*]—cardiac condition—I'm sorry, but there's only one word for it. [FREVILLE *instinctively covers his ears.*] Yes, yes—but I'm afraid we must face it —alarming. She might—she might fall dead at any moment.

FREVILLE:
Good God!

DOCTOR:
There is just this about it—the thing has never yet been taken seriously. Er—what age is she, Mr. Freville?

FREVILLE:
Forty-eight.

DOCTOR:
Precisely. With ladies one likes that little point corroborated. Comparatively young—the arteries—still elastic. Nauheim might do wonders for her, yet.

FREVILLE:

Nauheim—in Germany?

DOCTOR:

It has that misfortune, but what they don't know there about the heart is not known. I haven't alarmed her; she must not be alarmed.

FREVILLE:

You can't alarm Blanche about *herself*. She never thinks about herself at all.

DOCTOR:

Quite—I'm sure—very sweet woman.

FREVILLE:

My God! But what is it?

DOCTOR:

The technical word wouldn't convey much to you, I'm afraid. But it comes to this—some sudden excitement, some extra strain, and the heart might give out with no more warning than a cigar gives you when it stops drawing. [FREVILLE *gives a furtive look at the cigar in his hand.*]

FREVILLE:

But—but we'd no idea. Invalidish, anæmic, all that, but this is utterly beyond anything——

DOCTOR:

That is not uncommon. It's part of the tragedy of these cases. The thing should have been taken in hand much earlier, but even as it is, with care and the Nauheim treatment, I don't see why she shouldn't see sixty yet. As I say, the great thing is not to alarm her—to keep her from worry and excitement, and to get her to Nauheim at once.

FREVILLE [*distracted*]:

Yes, yes! Of course! Look here, doctor, do you mind

telling my son and daughter? I—positively—I don't feel up to it. Did you mention the heart to my wife?

DOCTOR:

I told Mrs. Freville she was so run down that there was a certain sluggishness we should have to get rid of.

FREVILLE:

We're not to go beyond that? All right—all right—only—— Good God!

DOCTOR:

Quite! But while there's life—I could tell you of a case very similar—and she went on—she went on, I think, nineteen years before she—er—went off. Heart disease is extraordinarily varied, Mr. Freville; that's what makes it so extremely interesting. I knew another case—he was in the Blues; one of his valves was practically a passenger. I gave him six months of a quiet life—do you know—that fellow gave me the shock of my life; he went through the war.

FREVILLE:

Did he? Splendid! And you think my wife might——

DOCTOR [*with a smile*]:

Mr. Freville, in these cases we hope for the best and er —prepare for the worst. I am ordering her digitalis; but the great thing first and last is Nauheim. For heart, and eye treatment, nothing like Germany, I'm afraid.

FREVILLE:

Oh! Germany—it's all the same to me; but—er— there's the journey! Surely——

DOCTOR:

A little oscillation is no bad thing in such a case. Don't worry about that, Mr. Freville. Keep her warm and well fed, but lightly—lightly; for stimulant a thimbleful of brandy now and then; no heavy wines. A leetle cup of black coffee with sugar—sugar is alcohol—twice a day, will assist. The dear lady is so little concerned about herself, that we must help her, Mr. Freville; we must help her.

FREVILLE [*with his hand to his head*]:
I should think so. She is—well, I can't tell you what she is to us all.

DOCTOR:
I'm sure, I'm sure. The presence in the house; the bird that lays the golden eggs. Quite! By the way, I rather advise celibacy.

FREVILLE [*rolling his eyes*]:
Yes, yes, yes, yes. As a matter of fact—er——

DOCTOR [*after pausing for a finish that does not come*]:
Tell me one thing. Are you aware of any complex? [*Smiling*] Without laying stress on the new cult, we—er —are not above accepting a wrinkle, Mr. Freville.

FREVILLE:
D'you mean was she startled before she was born, or something of that sort?

DOCTOR [*still smiling*]:
A leetle extreme. But has she any obsession, any pet alarm of any kind?

FREVILLE:
I don't think so. She's very placid; always has been.

DOCTOR:
Um!—Yes. Sometimes, you know, we have a mask to deal with. The more seemingly placid the greater the agitation; especially in these—er—selfless natures. Anything in the birth of her children—any domestic shock?

FREVILLE:
Only me, doctor.

DOCTOR [*with a little laugh*]:
Very good! You have a son and a daughter? They don't give anxiety?

FREVILLE:
No-o! They're—modern.

DOCTOR [*dubiously*]:
I see. And—er—where shall I find them?

FREVILLE:
In the dining-room. I'll show you. It's tremendously good of you, doctor. You can put it so much better than I can. I'm absolutely upset.

DOCTOR:
Don't let it appear, Mr. Freville. We must manage her, as the French say. I should like to see her again, when you come back from Nauheim.

FREVILLE [*laying an envelope on the table*]:
Of course, of course! [*He turns to a door on the left. The* DOCTOR, *as in a dream, pockets the envelope, and follows.*]

DOCTOR [*looking out of the window*]:
A charming position you have! This is the best month in London, I always think.

    They go out, but almost immediately FREVILLE *returns.*

FREVILLE [*to himself—at the table*]:
Good God—not to alarm her. Not to alarm her. [*He takes a cigar, nicks, lights it, and takes a good long whiff or two, closing his eyes; then goes to the drawing-room door and opens it.*] Well, darling? How did you like him?

BLANCHE FREVILLE *comes in with three roses and three carnations in a little jar. She is a very fragile woman, with a sweet, if slightly ironic, smile, extremely like what the doctor has called "a presence in the house."*

BLANCHE:
Oh! Quite nice for a doctor. Here's a clove pink for you, Gus. [*She pins it into his buttonhole.*] Would you like a marrow-bone at dinner?

FREVILLE [*carried away by the scent of the clove and the thought of marrow-bone*]:
Wouldn't I? Bless you! [*Taking her by the ephemeral shoulders*] He thinks you're dreadfully run down.

BLANCHE:
My dear, they always do. It's the hobby of doctors. *Parlons d'autres choses.* What are you going to do this afternoon?

FREVILLE [*sidelong*]:
Well, I—er—rather thought of going to see some Chinese lacquer at the British Museum. We're publishing a book on it, you know.

BLANCHE [*with a look that he does not see, indulgent, half-whimsical, half-malicious*]:
That'll be very nice. Perfect day for lacquer. The light is exquisite.

FREVILLE:
That fellow says that Nauheim would buck you up, Blanche. One ought to do what they suggest, don't you think?

BLANCHE:
My dear, he's given me some stuff; I think that's indulging him quite enough.

FREVILLE:

That's naughty.

BLANCHE [*quizzical*]:

Are you so anxious to go to Nauheim?

FREVILLE:

I? I'm anxious that you should go. It might be a little difficult for me to get away just yet. But Nonny could take you, and I could join you there. Or Roger—he gets ten days at Whitsuntide.

BLANCHE:

My dear, I think you'll all be happier at home. These places are no catch. Nauheim sounds particularly dull. They have to suggest something, you know.

FREVILLE:

That's true, of course. But still, anything that'll do you good!

.   .   .   .

1925 or 1926.

SIMILES

AN UNFINISHED PLAY IN THREE ACTS

CHARACTERS

JOHN BARLEY	.	.	A Hairdresser
MR. JONES	.	.	His Victim
MONA CURTIS	.	.	A Face and Hand Specialist
ARTHUR LEPPEDGE	.	.	A Stockbroker
HELEN LEPPEDGE	.	.	His Wife
CADGMAN	.	.	A Taxi Driver
MR. FROLLING	.	.	A Pawnbroker
WALSH	.	.	The Leppedges' Maid

ACT I

MADAME LILA'S *hairdressing establishment. The men's room. Thursday, 12.30 noon.*

ACT II

The LEPPEDGES' *flat near the Albert Hall. Thursday, 12.45 noon.*

ACT III

The same. Friday morning.

Kensington, early August. Time: The present.

ACT I

The men's hairdressing room in MADAME LILA'S *hair-dressing establishment in Kensington. It is not a large affair, and is fitted with three basins and the usual appurtenances. One assistant is on his holiday, another is at his lunch, the third and chief assistant,* JOHN BARLEY, *is at work on* MR. JONES, *who is lathered up to the eyes.* JOHN BARLEY *is a shortish stocky man with a hardwood face and toothbrush moustache.*

BARLEY [*stropping a razor*]:
I've never seen an 'orse race, but I can pick winners all right.

MR. JONES [*struggling a little with the lather*]:
How do you do it?

BARLEY [*regarding him—razor suspended*]:
I'm not bothered with appearances. Some see an 'orse —think it looks pretty and go and back it. All 'orses look pretty when they're slicked up. There used to be a song: "The women, I am told"—and then a line endin' in "old"—"for catchin' men 'ave many a tricky way— they've a colour like the rose—but when that colour goes —'ow different they look by light o' day." [*Approaching the upper lip with the razor and nipping the nostrils*] Not up, I suppose?

MR. JONES [*nasally*]:
No.

BARLEY [*shaving*]:
What we get shaved for, I don't know. Naturally a mass of 'air—I read in *Tit-Bits* or was it *John Bull?*— all the same so far as accuracy goes—that if the nation

249

stopped shavin'—million adults, allowin' for beavers—
there'd be an 'undred million minutes a day saved. One
million six 'undred and sixty-six thousand, six 'undred and
six hours a day, or say nine million hours a week—nine by
fifty—four 'undred and fifty million labour hours a year
—all gone down the drain, to make us look pretty. [*Fin-
ishes the upper lip, and pauses.*] They say that would build
four 'undred and fifty new St. Paulses every year. Or
put it another way: The working day is three 'undred and
sixty minutes. Ten minutes added to that would throw
another man out of every thirty-six on the dole. We'd
all be cave men and there'd be two 'undred and fifty
thousand extra unemployed. Look at the Arabs—all beavers and all unemployed. But all this beautification! These
red nails the women are goin' in for—d'you like 'em?

MR. JONES:
    No.

BARLEY:
    Why make 'em red when they're naturally pink?

MR. JONES:
    Exactly!

BARLEY:
    And look at 'air lotions. Gloss! First you shampoo the
gloss off, and then you stick it on again! Why not keep
your natural oil? What about Absalom or Lady Godiva,
or Merlin or Elijah? The ravens came and nested in 'is
beard.

MR. JONES:
    No, no; they fed him.

BARLEY:
    The Old Testament. Was it 'im who went up in a
chariot of fire? Or Elisha? Very like, those two. All

these old tales, nursery rhymes. I'm thankful I wasn't brought up at my mother's knee.

MR. JONES:

But about those winners?

BARLEY:

You want to know my system? I go on the fact that they're all crooks except the 'orses.

MR. JONES [*shocked*]:
What?

BARLEY:

Lord Blankey and the other dukes that 'ave got nothin' to gain—d'you think they're allowed to race straight? Too many o' these trainers and jockeys an' stable 'ands about 'em. If you know a man's rock-bottom honest, you've got 'im.

MR. JONES:

Cynical that, isn't it?

BARLEY:

I keep my eyes open; never believe what I'm told. Take the daily papers. You don't believe 'em, do you?

MR. JONES:

Not always.

BARLEY:

Better never.

MR. JONES:

What—*The Watch?*

BARLEY:

Watch!—You can believe *The Watch* when the news doesn't go against its interests. *The Watch* maintains the stettis quo. You can't trust any paper to give both sides full value. A man stands up for 'imself. 'Tisn't 'is business to keep 'is opponent on 'is feet. Shave be'ind the ears?

MR. JONES:
No.

BARLEY:
Some people abuse the papers; I don't. There might be something to be said for juggin' the lot; but short o' that you must take 'em as they come.

MR. JONES:
Do you ever read *The Watch?*

BARLEY:
Not to say read. Take it up once in a while when it's left in the Tube. Always the same. While I trim your 'air, would you like your 'ands seen to, Mr. Jones?

MR. JONES:
The same girl that did them last time?

BARLEY:
Miss Curtis. I'll see if she's free.

    He goes to the door at back. MR. JONES *thoughtfully fingers his chins.* BARLEY *returns.*

BARLEY:
Comin' in a minute.

MR. JONES [*touching his back hair*]:
There's too much just here.

BARLEY:
Ah! You won't grow any more on the top. You've got to the stettis quo there. Anne Domine.

MR. JONES [*with a slight wry smile*]:
Had your holiday?

BARLEY [*aproning him*]:
Always take it early September; better fishin' then. It's sport makes life worth livin'. [*Goes for neck clippers.*]

MR. JONES:
Others think work, I believe; others think women.

BARLEY [*grinning*]:
Work? Well, you've got to work if you want to eat. But women? Work and women cancel each other out. Sport's the only real thing.

MR. JONES:
Fishermen's stories, for instance?

BARLEY:
'Eard of the man 'oo's wife 'ad a baby? 'E'd been listenin' to fishermen's stories and someone asked 'im when 'e was goin' fishin' 'imself. 'E shook 'is 'ead an' said: "No; my wife's just 'ad a baby." "What weight?" said the other. . . . "Twenty-four pound." . . . But you've 'eard it?

MR. JONES:
Yes.

BARLEY:
Um! Those chestnuts are very artificial. [*Runs the clipper up the neck.*]

MR. JONES [*wincing*]:
Those clippers are real enough; and so's my hair.

BARLEY:
You've been touchin' this with a razor.

MR. JONES:
The edges—yes.

BARLEY [*taking up his scissors and snapping them*]:
Just a trim, I suppose. [*Swings* MR. JONES *full face.*]

MONA CURTIS *enters; a pretty girl, carrying her equipment, and looking pale. She draws up a stool, sits on it, and takes one of* MR. JONES's *hands.* BARLEY *snips. A silence.*

MR. JONES:

What do you think of that expression: "Straight from the horse's mouth"?

BARLEY [*with a little dry laugh*]:

American. 'Ome of advertisement an' skyscrapers. I 'ad an American in yesterday. Very bitter about stocks an' shares. [*He suspends the scissors.*] Before the crisis, 'e said, there 'adn't been an issue of capital for years over there that 'ad the slightest relation to reality. I forget 'ow 'e put it—somethin' like the brokers reachin' down the glory, an' waterin' the stock out o' the wells of their imaginations. Same over 'ere, you know. The front they put on some o' these issues—all face-aid.

> *He goes on snipping, and* MONA *pauses a secona to give him a faintly smiling look.*

Look at Kreuger—there was a bluff! Took everybody in —includin' himself.

MR. JONES:

Took me in all right.

BARLEY:

All done by charm, they say. Enjoyed 'isself an' then —pop!—an' left 'em all in the soup. If the truth was known nothin's worth its market valyer. . . . Think that's enough off, Mr. Jones? 'Ave a look be'ind. [*Holding a hand mirror to the back hair.*]

MR. JONES:

Yes, I think.

BARLEY:

Flowers and 'oney? [*Taking up the bottle*] There's an example. You could sell anything with that name. [*To* MONA] What 'ave you got there? Sweet almond paste! 'Oo could resist that? It's all in a name. Look at that Golden 'Air colt last year. Change 'is name an' he gets rheumatism. [*Sprinkling* MR. JONES's *head*] Machine or 'and brush?

MR. JONES:
Just comb it, please; back all round.

BARLEY:
You're right. D'you think I'd 'ave one of these brushes on my 'ead? They're fresh-washed, of course. [*Combs the hair.*] That right? [MR. JONES *nods.*] While you're 'avin' your 'ands finished, you'll like me to see what Captain Jinks is tippin' for to-day.

He goes over to a corner where on a table are three or four newspapers.

MR. JONES [*to the girl*]:
Had a busy week?

MONA:
Pretty good—considering.

MR. JONES:
You look as if you wanted a holiday.

MONA:
So I do.

MR. JONES:
Feeling the heat?

MONA:
It's my nerves.

MR. JONES:
D'you know what you remind me of?

MONA:
No.

MR. JONES:
A tobacco flower. [*At her look of surprise*] You know

them? Very charming, pale, smell sweet, but inclined to flop.

MONA [*with a rather sickly smile*]:
Now the other hand, please.

BARLEY [*returning*]:
'Ere you are! Silverside for the three o'clock, and Pop goes for the four-thirty. I don't think you'll better that, to-day.

MR. JONES:
I shan't try. I see now how you spot your winners.

BARLEY:
Study the papers, and get to learn which o' the tipsters 'as been out o' luck—then follow 'im.

MR. JONES:
And drop him?

BARLEY:
When 'e drops you. 'E won't be long. Some people like an 'orse's name. Some take a fancy to a jockey, or a trainer, or even an owner. I've heard of men only bettin' on Fridays. No use. A tipster 'as got to be right now and then, or 'e'd lose 'is job. Just men like you an' me, makin' their livin'. Watch for 'im to 'ave a losin' sequence, then at his first winner follow 'im. They don't 'ide their lights under bushels—these captains—Captain This and Captain That and Captain The Other—never get beyond the rank of captain. There was a major once, but 'e called 'imself "The General." Military rank! Every profession 'as its face-aid. Never believe an 'airdresser 'oo says your 'air'll grow again; you might as well believe in these artificial pearls.

MONA *drops the hand she is working on, gives a jerk, and takes the hand up again.*

MR. JONES:

If I've got time I'll test your theory. When I go racing I like to back my own judgment.

BARLEY [*shaking his head*]:

No; even the 'orse knows more than you do. Then there's all these poker-faced fellows waitin' to take you in.

MR. JONES [*to* MONA]:

Well, thank you. That seems a good hand, now. [*He regains possession of it and gets out of his chair.*] How much will that be altogether?

BARLEY:

Ninepence the shave—shillin' the 'air—two shillin's the 'ands—three and nine. [*Receiving five shillings*] Thank you.

MR. JONES:

Good morning! [*To* MONA] Good morning! [*Receives his hat and goes.*]

BARLEY:

I didn't offend 'im, did I? 'E couldn't think of an answer—that was it. Nice man. [*Putting his basin to rights.*]

MONA [*stopping at the door*]:
Mr. Barley——

BARLEY:

I can always talk to 'im. Modest—except about 'is judgment. Funny 'ow racing goes to a man's 'ead.

MONA:
Mr. Barley——

BARLEY:
Eh!

MONA:
I'm in trouble.

BARLEY:
Nothin' old-fashioned, I 'ope.

MONA [*coming from the door*]:
No. But I don't know what to do.

BARLEY:
Not unusual.

MONA:
There's a lady—Mrs. Leppedge——

BARLEY:
Ah! A bright bit—good deal of face-aid about 'er.

MONA:
She's pretty.

BARLEY:
Matter o' taste. Well?

MONA:
She was in yesterday afternoon.

BARLEY:
Repairs and redecorations.

MONA:
She had her face and neck creamed and massaged. And when she'd gone I saw she'd left her pearls.

BARLEY:
Mocks.

MONA:
Oh, no! Real pearls.

BARLEY:
You can't tell.

MONA:
These were real. If they hadn't been I wouldn't have done what I did.

BARLEY [*eyeing her pallor*]:
Well! What did you do? Tell Madame Lila?

MONA:
I didn't notice them at first. Then I took them up and felt them, and that gave me the idea—so silky! I just slipped my scarf over them, in case she should come back for them. But she didn't, and I thought: "Well, now she can't do anything till the shop opens to-morrow morning." So I made believe they were in a drawer where I could find them in the morning, and—and I took them away with me.

BARLEY:
What for?

MONA:
I was going to a dance, and my young man was to be there, and I thought I'd wear them just for that evening. You do get sick of similes, don't you?

BARLEY:
Can't say—never 'ad any.

MONA:
They did suit me! But when I got home and put my hand up to my neck, they weren't there.

BARLEY:
Pinched?

MONA [*distressed*]:
I don't know. It's awful, Mr. Barley. What am I to do? I can't go asking openly about them, because they weren't mine. If Madame Lila plumps it out at me, I'll never be able to bluff her. There was nobody but me in the room where Mrs. Leppedge was attended to.

BARLEY:
No enquiry this morning?

MONA:

Not yet. But I'm dead scared. Who's going to believe I took them just to wear at a dance?

BARLEY:

Anyone who knows women, and that's not many. What d'you want me to do—believe you?

MONA:

I hardly slept all night, and whenever I woke up I wished I was dreaming.

BARLEY:

If they was reel (and if they wasn't she'd pretend they was), what should you say they was worth?

MONA:

Oh—I don't know; a thousand pounds or more.

BARLEY:

Been round to where you were dancin'?

MONA:

Yes. Nothing's been picked up.

BARLEY:

Who's your young man?

MONA:

Cortin and Cozens.

BARLEY:

Electric light fittin's. 'Im?

MONA:

Haven't had a chance; and I wouldn't like him to know.

BARLEY:

Given to practical jokes?

MONA:

No.

BARLEY:
Where'd you leave him last night?

MONA:
At my door—he took me home.

BARLEY:
Did he notice the pearls?

MONA:
Yes; he said you'd think they were real.

BARLEY:
Why should this woman pitch on you?

MONA:
I took the pearls off her neck.

BARLEY:
She might 'ave done a dozen things after she left here.
I should say she couldn't be certain.

MONA:
She took a taxi from the door, and I heard her say
"Albert Hall Mansions," and I know that's where she
lives.

BARLEY:
Dropped 'em in the cab—that's what she did. It's not
for you to accuse yourself. Wait till someone does it for
you.

MONA:
I wish I'd never seen the wretched things.

BARLEY [*beckoning to her*]:
You look me in the face. Are you makin' a case for
yourself, or tellin' the truth?

MONA:
Telling the truth.

BARLEY:

Well, don't you do it to anyone else. It can be used against you. You sit tight. It's early closin' to-day. Twelve forty-five already. Where's Madame?

MONA:

Gone to Gustave's about a transformation.

BARLEY:

Ash-blonde, ⹁ suppose. This sunburn—women are crazy now to be what they aren't.

MONA:

Mr. Barley, d'you think I might pretend it's one o'clock?

BARLEY:

I shouldn't. Put a face on it. They've got no evidence. You sit down an' give yourself a touch o' sunburn. You look like a ghost.

MONA:

Sunburned ghost [*with a ghostly laugh*].

The telephone rings.

Oh! Oh! I can't. Mr. Barley.

BARLEY:

It's probably Madame to say she won't be back.

MONA:

No; I can't. Mr. Barley, quick, or the girl will be coming.

BARLEY:

All right, all right! [*Moves to the telephone.*] Just stand by. [*He takes up the receiver.*] 'Allo! . . . Ye-s —Madame Lila's. 'Oo is it? Leppedge? [*Gives* MONA *a look.*] Mrs.—Mrs. Leppedge—ye-es? . . . No, Madame's out. . . . Won't be back—early closin' to-day. . . . 'Oo's speakin'? Barley—'ead assistant—men's department. . . . 'Old the line a minute. [*Covering the phone—to* MONA] She wants the girl that did her face and neck yesterday.

MONA:
Oh!

BARLEY:
Don't dither—don't dither! Shall I say you're out?

MONA:
Yes—no.

BARLEY:
Well, which? They ain't the same.

MONA:
Oh! Advise me, Mr. Barley!

BARLEY:
Say you'll 'ave a look, and if you can't find 'em, you'll let her know. 'Ere, come to the phone. [MONA *approaches, and he transfers the receiver to her.*]

MONA:
Yes, Madam? . . . [*Listening*] Really, Madam?

BARLEY [*sotto voce*]:
Put some pep in it.

MONA [*louder*]:
Yes, Madam. Shall I have a look round? . . . Yes, I seem to remember taking them off; but are you sure you didn't put them on, afterwards? . . . Really, Madam, I don't think it's possible they could have been left.

BARLEY:
That's better. Rub it in.

MONA:
Let me have a look round, Madam. What is your number? . . . Kensington 80—oo—o. Yes, Madam. [*She abandons the receiver, and puts her hand to her heart.*]

BARLEY:

Well, you needn't look for 'em; that's one thing. We can spend the time inventin' the best face-aid. Pity you can't speak to her as one woman to another. 'As she an 'usband?

MONA [*faintly*]:

Yes.

BARLEY:

He gave 'em to her, I expect. Men do funny things. All you've got to do is to say we can't find 'em.

MONA:

If she suggests coming round . . .

BARLEY:

Five minutes to one? Tell 'er we'll be closed. Say Madame always closes to the tick. Better! Say you'll come round and see her.

MONA:

Oh! I couldn't.

BARLEY:

I'll come with you. Take the bull by the 'orns. You leave it to me when we get there.

MONA:

I dread——

BARLEY:

All you've got to do is to sound a bit breathless. [*Goes to the telephone.*] 'Allo! Madame Lila's speakin'. . . . 'Old the line. [*To* MONA] Come on—breathless. [*She takes the line from him.*]

MONA:

I—I've looked and asked everywhere, Madam. No sign of them. . . . No, Madam. . . . No. It's just closing time. . . . [BARLEY *prompts her with a nudge and a shake of the head.*] We have to close sharp by law. Would—would [*again* BARLEY *nudges her and nods*]—you like me and the head assistant to come round and see you instead——?

BARLEY [*sotto voice*]:
At once.

MONA:
At once. . . . Certainly, Madam; a pleasure, Madam. . . . No trouble, Madam. . . . 404 Albert Hall Palace Court Mansions; yes, Madam. [*Replaces the receiver.*]

BARLEY:
'Albert 'All Palace Court Mansions'—the poor fish! [*He regards* MONA, *who is leaning against the wall with her eyes closed.*] Cheerio—you did that well. The thing is to give the impression that we're more anxious to get 'em back than she is 'erself. No pretence there—they're bound to be insured for more than they're worth. Come back 'ere, and mind you put on a soupson o' sunburn, an' touch up your lips.

MONA:
I shall never go through with it, Mr. Barley.

BARLEY:
Oh, yes, you will! We'll stop at Smart's an' get you a dose o' sal volatile. That'll buck you up. [*He pats her shoulder.*] Put a face on it.

MONA *covers her lips with her hand, and goes out.*

BARLEY *busies himself with the putting to rights of his department—singing,* "*They've a colour like the rose —but when that colour goes—'ow different they look by light o' day.*"

Girls! She 'asn't got the brass of most of 'em nowadays.

He washes his hands and takes up a hand mirror to make sure that his toothbrush moustaches stop exactly at

*the corners of his lips, takes a razor and squares the hair
at the ears; slips off his apron, and dons his jacket and
billycock hat, then closes the shop door. He is now ready,
and takes up the paper.*

I shall 'ave a bob on those two both ways. Now where's
that girl? [*Calling*] Miss Curtis! Oh! 'Ere you are!
That's better. Now remember; she don't know a thing;
just make a straight lip of it. Keep it off yourself, and on
to the establishment—impersonal. Remember I'm the boss
in Madame Lila's absence. Shove it on to me. Other girl
gone? [MONA *nods.*] And all closed? [MONA *nods.*]
Well, we'll go out at the back. Mind, the first you knew
of it was 'er ringing up this morning; and whatever you
say, stick to it. You can't go pale in that complexion, can
you?

MONA:
   I could faint in it.

BARLEY:
   Well, don't! Unless you'd like to get it over before we
start. [*There is the sound of a taxi stopping, and the ring
of a bell.* MONA *gives a gasp.* BARLEY *sidesteps to the shop
right and squints round.*]

BARLEY [*nodding—in a whisper*]:
   Can't see. Lucky we'd gone. [*The bell rings again.*]
Ring away!

MONA [*whispering*]:
   She can't see in, can she?

BARLEY:
   Nao; but we'd better wait. 'Ere, stand straight! Catch
'old o' my shoulder. [*There is a sharp tapping on the
door.*] Knock away. When a shop's shut, it *is* shut.

MONA:
   Hadn't we better open and get it over?

BARLEY:

And throw away the good impression? She's bound to go back and wait for us. We'll be there almost before her. Supposin' it *is* 'er carryin' on outside. Besides, you've got to 'ave that dope. [*Once more the bell is rung, and there is a sharp tapping.*]

MONA [*gasping—her nerves all ragged*]:
Oh! Hell!

BARLEY:
That's better! But that's the last time, you'll see.
Both listen. There is the sound of a taxi starting.

BARLEY:
Right away! We can go now. [*Looking at the clock*] She only missed us by a minute and an 'alf. We'll get that dope, take a bus, and be there in a quarter of an hour. What's she want these pearls for in such an 'urry? Looks as if they really was real. On the other 'and, if they was, she'd rather 'ave the value.

MONA:
They were real.

BARLEY:
'Ow do you know? You never 'ad any.

MONA:
It's the feel.

BARLEY:
Fiddle! Come along, my girl!

He leads towards the door on the left. MONA takes a long breath, braces herself, and follows.

ACT II

SCENE I

The LEPPEDGES' *flat in Albert Hall Palace Court Mansions; a tastefully furnished green-panelled room; twelve forty-five on the same morning.* HELEN LEPPEDGE, *a well-built nicely preserved young woman, is standing by the telephone.*

HELEN:

No; all the better. And you? . . . Good. . . . I say, do you remember if I had any pearls on last night? . . . No? Damn! He'll be back before lunch. He always notices little things, especially when he's given them to me. . . . Yes, darling; but could you possibly go round to Paulati's, or telephone, asking whether they've been picked up? And would you look round at home? That would be frightfully nice of you. And would you phone me? . . . Oh! And if it should be a male voice, ask his number and say it's the wrong one. . . . Wasn't it divine? . . .

ARTHUR LEPPEDGE, *about forty years old, of square and substantial build, stands listening.*

HELEN [*noticing*]:

Well, good-bye, darling. [*Cuts off.*]

ARTHUR:

What's divine?

HELEN:

A dress at Jay's we saw yesterday.

ARTHUR:

And who is a darling?

HELEN:

Maud. Aren't you a bit early?

268

ARTHUR:
Tubby drove me up.

HELEN:
Anybody try to vamp you at Maidenhead?

ARTHUR [*approaching her*]:
You're looking very fresh. Give me a kiss.

HELEN [*holding up a creamy cheek*]:
I do dislike cigary kisses.

ARTHUR:
What's happened to your neck?

HELEN:
Nothing.

ARTHUR [*with his head on one side and a round eye*]:
Pearls?

HELEN:
Yes; I've mislaid them.

ARTHUR:
You've——!

HELEN:
Don't get in a stew, because that'll be two stews in one morning.

ARTHUR:
Mislaid? How d'you mean—lost?

HELEN:
For the moment.

ARTHUR:
Do you know they cost about twelve hundred?

HELEN:
Awful, isn't it?

ARTHUR:
When did you miss them?

HELEN:

I don't really know. I don't seem to remember them one way or the other till I got up this morning. You don't— little things you wear every day.

ARTHUR:

When was the last time you noticed the pearls yesterday?

HELEN:

Well, if I had them on, I must have had them off at the hairdresser's.

ARTHUR:

Why?

HELEN:

Because I had my neck done.

ARTHUR:

When?

HELEN:

About tea-time.

ARTHUR:

You mean you can't remember whether you had them on at all yesterday?

HELEN:

I'm pretty sure I had them on till I went to the hair-dresser's.

ARTHUR:

Have you asked there?

HELEN:

I was just going to get them. I've only been out of bed half an hour.

ARTHUR:

Taking it out.

HELEN:
   Yes; I had a tremendous dissipation.

ARTHUR:
   What?

HELEN:
   Prom—all English composers. Most emotionalising.

ARTHUR:
   Try the Queen's Hall, then.

HELEN [*dialling*]:
   There's that high buzzing.

ARTHUR:
   Replace the receiver.

HELEN [*languidly*]:
   London's just full of people shooting grouse and ringing up the Queen's Hall. [*Dialling again*] Yes. . . . Is that the Queen's Hall? Can you tell me, please, if a pearl necklace has been picked up from last night? I was sitting in the Grand Circle, row three, near the centre. . . . Nothing at all picked up? . . . You're sure. Thank you. [*To her husband*] They must get that answer by heart.

ARTHUR:
   Did you try a dress on at Jay's?

HELEN:
   No. We were looking at advance models.

ARTHUR:
   And from there, where did you go?

HELEN:
   Straight to the hairdresser's.

ARTHUR:
   Well, get *them*. [HELEN *looks for the number*.] Seems to me you make very light of those pearls.

HELEN [*with a faint mockery*]:

Oh! no, darling. [*Dialling*] Is that Madame Lila's?
. . . Mrs. Leppedge speaking. . . . Is Madame Lila in? . . .
Will she be long? . . . Who is speaking? . . . I see. I
should like to speak to the girl who did my face and neck
yesterday, please. [*A longish wait, during which* ARTHUR
comes closer.] Is that Miss Curtis? You remember doing
my neck yesterday. I've missed my pearls. . . . I was wondering whether I left them. . . . They must have been off my
neck when it was being done. . . . No, I don't. But if you
remember taking them off. . . . I think I must have left
them. . . . Kensington eight o, double o, o.

ARTHUR:

What's her voice like?

HELEN:

Quavery.

ARTHUR:

What's she doing now?

HELEN:

Having a look round.

ARTHUR:

Or pretending to be.

HELEN:

Arthur, you are horrid.

ARTHUR:

Well, why should she quaver?

HELEN:

You'd quaver if someone were suspecting you of cheat-
ing at cards.

ARTHUR:

Oh! bosh! Look here, say you'll come round.

HELEN [*into the mouthpiece*]:

No. . . . Madame Lila's not come in? . . . And you say she won't be back? Early closing. . . . Yes, that will do perfectly. . . . You're sure it's not troubling you? . . . My address is 404 Albert Hall Palace Court Mansions. [*She replaces the receiver.*]

ARTHUR:

What's that?

HELEN:

She and the chief man assistant are coming round.

ARTHUR:

Why should they, unless they're putting up a bluff? If I were you I'd jump into a taxi; you'd be there by one.

HELEN:

Oh, no! I must wait for them, now.

ARTHUR:

I don't see—if you're slippy.

HELEN [*decidedly*]:

No. [*A thought strikes her.*] *You* go, and say I sent you, to save them the trouble. It's your funeral.

ARTHUR:

Mine! H'm! Well, I *will* go.

HELEN:

Good, darling! I'm sure you're wise.

ARTHUR *gives her a look, as if saying "I never know where you're getting off," and goes out.*

HELEN [*quietly*]:

Thank God! [*Opens the door an inch, listens for the clang of the lift door; goes to the telephone and dials.*] Hallo? Yes. . . . Any news of the pearls? . . . No? Oh! . . . He's back; full of hearty Maidenhead air—but I've got him on the run for the moment. I wanted to save you

lying on the phone. The P.M.G. doesn't like it. Neither
lying nor love-making; he has good principles. . . . Yes,
darling, but I *said* he had. . . . You realised that the last
"darling," when I cut off before, wasn't for you. . . . You
can't imagine how quick he was noticing the undisguised
purity of my neck. . . . Well, as a fact, he's running about
London at the moment seeing impurities everywhere. . . .
Yes, but, what I was going to say was: This is going to take
me all my time; and if I don't get them back it's going to
take me still more time. So everything's off until I phone
you again. . . . Abso*lute*ly, darling. . . . But abso*lute*ly,
bless you! [*She makes the sound of a kiss with her lips and
touches them with her finger.*] [*To herself*] How perfectly marvellous it will be when you can see by television
how he looks when you blow him a kiss. Only, will he—
by then? [*Aware that the door has been opened.*]

WALSH:
At what time lunch, Madam?

HELEN:
Well, Walsh, what with one thing and another, I should
say—two-ish.

WALSH:
Then I'd better call the soufflé off, Madam.

HELEN:
Yes. But bring in some sherry—four glasses.

WALSH:
The old sherry, Madam?

HELEN [*with a smile*]:
Unless there's any older. How melancholy it is that one
dies before sherry's fit to drink.

WALSH:
Yes, Madam.

HELEN:

My grandfather always sent his best sherry to the West Indies for at least two voyages; but I never knew whether being rolled about made it less or more mellow.

WALSH:

Being rolled about, Madam?

HELEN:

And you've got to allow for the cask—I think they were rum casks—a sort of pickling. I feel that to be rolled about in a rum cask would have a distinct effect on me. [WALSH *giggles.*] By the way, had you realised that I've got no pearls on?

WALSH:

Yes, Madam.

HELEN:

How wonderful you are! Well, where are they? You haven't put them anywhere safe?

WALSH:

Next the skin for pearls, Madam, is safest.

HELEN:

That's what I think, day after day.

WALSH:

No one can't get at them there.

HELEN:

Not while one's morals are sound.

WALSH:

Madam?

HELEN:

Um—are there any salted almonds left?

WALSH:

Yes, Madam.

ARTHUR:
Blasted half-toothbrush?

HELEN:
When he comes on to his stand, he's to come round.

ARTHUR:
What's this sherry for?

HELEN [*taking up a glass*]:
I shall want my lunch before I get it.

ARTHUR:
I want mine now. [*Takes up another glass. The two sip and nibble.*] So you had a beano last night?

HELEN [*scenting awkward questions*]:
Yes. Who was down at Tubby's?

ARTHUR:
Oh! Nobody.

HELEN:
Who were the others? Who's Mrs. Tubby at the moment?

ARTHUR:
He keeps her very dark.

HELEN:
It's that little fair thing, Dorothy Somer. Was she there?

ARTHUR:
No. I mean—yes. But it's not her.

HELEN:
Did she tell you?

ARTHUR:
Well, as a fact—— [*Lights a cigarette.*] Have one? [HELEN *shakes her head with a smile.*] As a fact——

HELEN:
You've said that, my dear. No confessions.

ARTHUR:
Confessions? I——!

HELEN:
You know the word.

ARTHUR:
But look here——

HELEN:
That's quite enough.

ARTHUR:
D'you mean to say that because I said "As a fact"——

HELEN:
Twice; and didn't contradict it.

ARTHUR:
Really, Helen, I wish you'd be serious.

HELEN:
To be serious leads to all sorts of . . . divorce. Well,
who else was there?

ARTHUR [*sulkily*]:
I'm not a rubber-neck conductor.

HELEN [*head to one side*]:
Straight before you—Mr. Tubby Cartwright, fine old
specimen of Georgian architecture, wearing thin on the top
story. To his left, that delicate piece——

ARTHUR:
Shut up!

HELEN:
Isn't she a "piece"? [*The door is opened.*] Yes?

WALSH:
A Mr. Barley and a Miss Curtis, Madam.

HELEN:
Quite. Show them in, and cancel the empty glasses.

WALSH:
Yes, Madam.

> WALSH *goes out.* HELEN *crosses to the fireplace.*
> ARTHUR *sulkily regards her.*

> WALSH *returns, ushering in* BARLEY *and* MONA.

HELEN:
Very good of you to have come. Will you have some sherry? Arthur!

> *They take the glasses handed to them.*

BARLEY:
Your 'ealth. [*Tosses off the sherry.*] We thought it better to relieve your minds, seein' it's early closin'. Miss Curtis will give you a résumé.

HELEN:
Yes?

MONA [*uneasily*]:
Madam, as I told you on the phone——

BARLEY:
That's right.

MONA:
I've looked everywhere, and I'm quite sure they're not in the place.

BARLEY:
'Igh class of customer, ours.

HELEN [*smiling, and raising her eyebrows*]:
That's why we thought they might not be in the place.

BARLEY:
What's that?

HELEN [*suavely*]:
They're not big things, are they, Mr.—er——

BARLEY:

Barley.

HELEN:

Anybody could slip a handkerchief over them and spirit them away.

BARLEY:

That's why I came round meself. Miss Curtis—she's touchy; and there's two other girls besides 'er—one of them's on 'er 'oliday. And Madame Lila—well, you wouldn't expect Madame. Then there's meself and one other man assistant at the present time o' speakin'. Well, you wouldn't expect us, would you?

HELEN:

I wouldn't expect anyone, Mr. Barley, much less suspect them.

BARLEY:

Well, what I mean—we can't 'ave our characters under suspicion; so I thought you'd like to give us the once over. They weren't similes, were they? [*Fixes his hard little eyes on* HELEN.]

HELEN [*raising her eyebrows*]:

What do *you* say, Arthur? Were they similes?

ARTHUR:

I paid twelve hundred for them.

BARLEY:

Could I see the insurance policy?

ARTHUR [*about to say, "Damn his impudence!" restrains himself, and says*]:

I'll get it. [*He goes out.*]

BARLEY:

In these days nothing seems what it is. It's never worth goin' out of your way till you've proved you're dealin' with the original.

HELEN:

Quite true, Mr. Barley.

BARLEY [*mollified*]:

Why should anyone wear originals when they can get similes for a 'undreth part of the cost and no one the wiser? When you 'ave your pearls stolen these insurance companies 'ave to pay up, because they can't prove to your satisfaction that you 'adn't lost the originals.

HELEN:

I was going to ask you, Mr. Barley, how you prove to their satisfaction that you have?

BARLEY [*taken aback*]:

Well, you 'ave to allow for each other. Not that I'd allow much for an insurance company. You've got their policy, and you 'aven't got the pearls. That's your case.

HELEN:

I'll explain that to my husband; it seems simple.

BARLEY:

So it is, if you prefer the money. Depends on your 'usband. If you can get your 'usband to give you a string o' pearls every birthday, you've got a steady income; and you can go about in similes all the time, and no one the wiser.

> ARTHUR *returns, with a paper in his hand. He hands it to* BARLEY, *and turns suddenly to* MONA.

ARTHUR:

When you're doing a customer's face and neck—where do you lay the things down?

BARLEY [*by way of giving her time*]:

Where do you?

MONA:

On the little table along the wall. There's a tray.

BARLEY:

A receptacle.

ARTHUR:

What makes you think you laid them down there yesterday?

MONA:

I always do.

HELEN:

Any ear-rings?

MONA:

No, Madam; only those you've got on, and they were so tiny.

HELEN:

I didn't see any other girl yesterday.

BARLEY:

There *is* another girl.

MONA:

She'd gone. We're so slack, Madam.

HELEN:

What makes you think I had them on at all?

MONA:

Well, really, Madam, I don't know——I seem to remember seeing them.

BARLEY:

That's right. You can't speak to things you 'aven't noticed. The truth's the truth, and beyond that you can't go.

ARTHUR:

I had a sort of idea you could.

BARLEY:

'Ow's that?

HELEN:
Well, you've just been saying, Mr. Barley, that nothing is really what it looks like.

MONA [*slightly hysterical*]:
If you don't believe me——

BARLEY:
Now, now! Of course they believe you. I'm the chief assistant; anyone that doesn't believe you has got me to deal with.

MONA:
I got nothing but my word——

BARLEY:
Good enough for me is good enough for anybody. We're an 'igh-class concern.

WALSH *enters.*

WALSH:
The driver, Madam.

ARTHUR:
Bring him in.

HELEN:
Some more sherry, Walsh. Would you like another glass, Mr. Barley?

BARLEY:
Never refuse good stuff.

WALSH *takes out the salver.*

ARTHUR:
We shall get to the bottom of it now. Were you still in the shop when I came a few minutes ago?

BARLEY [*shaking his head*]:
I should say we'd just gone out. Once we're shut, we're shut.

WALSH *enters with the salver and sherry and three glasses.*

HELEN [*handing* BARLEY *a glass*]:
Not a simile—this, Mr. Barley?

BARLEY:
Good 'ealth. [*Tosses it off. To* MONA] Why don't you drink yours?

MONA *drinks her sherry.*

WALSH [*at the door*]:
Mr. Cadgman.

Enter the TAXI-DRIVER, *who wears a rigid little patch of dark hair square below his nose.*

HELEN [*recognising him*]:
You drove me home here yesterday, didn't you?

CADGMAN:
That's right, Ma'am, now I see you.

HELEN:
Will you——? [*Hands him a glass.*]

CADGMAN:
Thank you. [*Looks around him and tosses it off.*]

ARTHUR:
You know what we want you for?

CADGMAN:
Not an idea.

ARTHUR:
What do you do with things you pick up in your cab?

CADGMAN:
Things I pick up? Take 'em to Scotland Yard. But I don't pick up a thing in a blue moon.

ARTHUR:

Didn't pick up a string of pearls yesterday?

CADGMAN:

Pearls? Last time I picked up pearls, they was worth seven and six—so they told me at the Yard. Nobody claimed 'em, so I 'ad my trouble for nothing.

HELEN:

There was nothing left in the cab after you brought me here?

CADGMAN:

Well, nothing in 'er when I took 'er 'ome.

ARTHUR:

You looked her over?

CADGMAN:

I did; from top to bottom, and shook the floor-rug. Not a thing.

HELEN:

Can you remember your next fare after me?

CADGMAN:

Very well; I didn't 'ave none.

ARTHUR:

None?

CADGMAN:

None. I'd promised me girl to take 'er out. So I just ran the cab back to the garridge, tuned 'er up, as I said, and came away. Thank ye, Sir. [*He takes the remaining glass of sherry from* ARTHUR *and sucks it down.*]

ARTHUR:

That's that, then.

CADGMAN:

But I remember your lady well. I've driven 'er before.

[*Touches his Hitlerism.*] Before I 'ad this. [*A little loosened by the sherry.*] My girl seems to think this gives you character.

BARLEY:
   'Itler's, or Charlie Chaplin's?

HELEN:
   Both celebrities, Mr. Cadgman.

BARLEY:
   If I 'ad them in my shop for ten minutes, they wouldn't be. To think a man can make a name by choppin' the ends off 'is moustache, turnin' out one foot, wearin' a bowler 'at, and treadin' on dogs' tails shows ye what the world is. [*Disputatiously*] Well, if 'e didn't, who'd know 'im from you or me?

   *   *   *   *   *

1932.